THE NEW SAGA LIBRARY
GENERAL EDITOR: HERMANN PALSSON

Viga-Glums
Saga

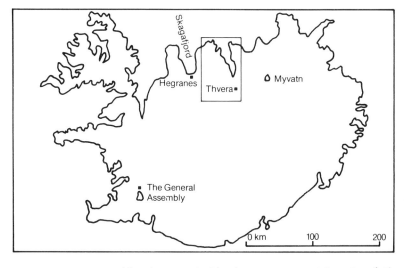

Map 1: ICELAND (for the area inside the square, see Maps 2 and 3)

Viga-Glums
Saga

WITH THE TALES OF
Ögmund Bash
AND
Thorvald Chatterbox

translated by
JOHN McKINNELL

Canongate/UNESCO

First published 1987 by
CANONGATE PUBLISHING LIMITED
17 Jeffrey Street, Edinburgh EH1 1DR

UNESCO COLLECTION OF REPRESENTATIVE WORKS
Icelandic Series
This work has been accepted in the
Icelandic Translation series of the United Nations
Educational, Scientific, and Cultural Organisation
(UNESCO)

British Library Cataloguing in Publication Data

Viga-Glums saga: with the tales of
Ögmund Bash and Thorvald Chatterbox.
1. Sagas
2. Old Norse prose literature—Translations into English
3. English prose literature—Translations from Old Norse
I. McKinnell, John, 1942–
839′.6808   PT7262.E5

ISBN 0-86241-0 84-3

The publisher acknowledges subsidy of
the Scottish Arts Council
towards the publication of this volume

Typeset by Witwell Limited, Liverpool
Printed and bound in Great Britain
by Biddles Limited, Guildford

Contents

Preface

This translation of *Viga-Glums saga* is based chiefly on an independent transcription of *Möðruvallabók*, the major authoritative manuscript, but I am also heavily indebted to two fine editions, by E.O.G. Turville-Petre (Oxford 1940, 2nd ed. 1960) and Jónas Kristjánsson (in *Íslenzk fornrit* IX, Reykjavík 1956).

The complete saga has been translated into English twice before, by Sir Edmund Head (London 1866) and by Lee M. Hollander (for the American Scandinavian Foundation, New York 1972), but both contain inaccuracies. Head had no good edition of the saga to work from, and Hollander's style is curiously uneven, perhaps because of his frankly admitted dislike for the text. No apology is therefore needed for a third translation, which I hope will show at least something of the saga's literary quality.

For the text of the two tales at the end of this volume, which both appear in the "Great" *Saga of Olaf Tryggvason*, I have generally followed *Íslenzk fornrit* IX, but have occasionally adopted readings footnoted there, where they improve the context or render into better English. *The Tale of Ögmund Bash* has been translated into English three times before: by J. Sephton, in his translation of the "Great" *Saga of Olaf Tryggvason* (London 1895), by Guðbrandur Vigfússon in *Origines Islandicae* (Oxford 1905), and by Hollander. *The Tale of Thorvald Chatterbox* has only previously been translated into English by Sephton.

Many people have helped me in the preparation of this book. I should like to thank Hið íslenzka Bókmenntafélag for permission to use maps 2 and 3, which are based on those in *Íslenzk fornrit* IX. Professor Hermann

Pálsson has made a large number of very helpful suggestions at every stage and saved me from many errors, though I am of course solely responsible for any that remain. Andy Dennis gave me much help with the legal aspect of the saga's narrative, and Stefán Karlsson supervised my work on the manuscript tradition with much kindness and patience.

I have received warm hospitality from the whole family at Munkaþverá, where most of the action of *Viga-Glums saga* takes place, and from Stefán Karlsson, Helga Ólufsdóttir and Steinunn Stefánsdóttir, in whose house in Reykjavík much of my first draft was written. Two secretaries, Mrs Marjorie Chesterton and Miss Maureen Smith, have re-typed my untidy drafts with great efficiency.

Last, but certainly not least, I am grateful to the late Professor Turville-Petre, who suggested many improvements to the first draft of this translation, on the shoulders of whose edition much of my material stands, and who was above all an inspiring teacher who did much to pass on to me his own love of early Icelandic literature.

J.S.M.
Durham
1986

Introduction

Versions and Origins

The complete text of *Víga-Glúms saga* survives in *Möðruvallabók*, (M.),[1] a large and attractive parchment codex from the mid 14th century, and as this is the only complete medieval text it has of necessity been followed in all translations, including this one. But fragments of a longer version appear in three leaves from MS AM 564a, 4to. and one from AM 445c, 4to., almost certainly all from the same undecorated copy, written in several hands about 1390.[2] The compressed text in M. appealed to the scholars of the romantic age, who in general held that the best and tersest sagas are the earliest; it thus seemed to represent best the saga's original form, while the fragments exemplified a later decline in taste. But Turville-Petre's introduction (pp. xxii–xxxii)[3] showed that in ch. 16, an interpolated episode also found in *Reykdæla saga*, the longer version in the fragment is much closer to *Reykdæla saga* than is the briefer text of M., which thus seems to be abridged from a longer original. The relationship between each of the other fragments and M. is of the same kind, and hence the fragments must represent the earlier stage of the text.

---

1. See the fine facsimile ed. by Ejnar Munksgaard in *Corpus Codicum Islandicorum Medii Ævi*, vol. 5, Copenhagen 1933, and the introduction by Einar Ólafur Sveinsson.
2. Stefán Karlsson, *Um Vatnshyrnu*, in *Opuscula* IV (*Bibliotheca Arnamagnæana* XXX) Copenhagen 1970, especially pp. 279–83 (English summary on p. 301); and in the same volume John McKinnell, *The Reconstruction of Pseudo-Vatnshyrna*, especially pp. 318–25.
3. *Víga-Glúms saga*, ed. E.O.G. Turville-Petre, Oxford 1940, 2nd ed., 1960.

But even the fragments do not show the saga in its original form, which seems not to have included chs. 13–16 (the Ingolf and Viga-Skuta episodes), both peripheral to the plot and sharing a distinctive style. In the Ingolf story, the major characters other than Glum are probably fictitious, the grasp of the law is slighter than in the rest of the saga, and the story owes something to fictional sources from outside Iceland (see below and Turville-Petre, Introduction pp. xxxiv-xxxv). The Skuta episode is equally clearly not original to the saga – only here is Glum called Viga-Glum, and *Reykdæla saga* ch. 26 tells the same story, as the end of a longer sequence of dealings between Skuta and Glum. The more circumstantial version in *Reykdæla saga* cannot simply be borrowed from *Viga-Glums saga*, but the story is just as out of place in both sagas, and has probably been independently interpolated into both.

Between these two episodes, the longer version of *Viga-Glums saga* includes a fragment of the story of Ögmund, considerably abbreviated compared with the version translated here, and with its essential chronology inconsistently altered (see *The Tale of Ögmund Bash*, note 3). This too probably originated as a short story on its own, for it has no great relevance in either of the sagas in which it now appears.

These additions were probably not made by the author of *Viga-Glums saga* himself from pre-existing sources, for both the Ingolf and the Ögmund story use other parts of the saga as source material – in the Ingolf episode, the quarrel at a horse-fight (cf. ch. 18), the gift of some wall-hangings (cf. ch. 1), and possibly Glum's domineering behaviour over the marriage of someone else's daughter (cf. ch. 11). In the Ögmund story, the opening genealogy is probably taken from *Viga-Glums saga* ch. 5, and Ögmund's origins appear to be connected with the maligned slaves of ch. 7. But there are no such indications in the Skuta story; and the common style of the Ingolf and Skuta episodes is shared to a large degree by ch. 26 of *Reykdæla saga*, and thus proves nothing about the common authorship of these interpolations.

The dating of anonymous sagas is difficult, and attempts to date *Viga-*

Glums saga by showing borrowings from other sagas into it or by other sagas from it have proved inconclusive.[4] Comparison has been made with works by Snorri Sturluson – chs. 33 and 108 of his *Saga of Olaf Tryggvason* and ch. 84 of his *Saga of St Olaf*, (where the resemblance is probably only coincidence) – but it is worth noting that the versions of verses 8 and 12 quoted in Snorri's *Edda* (ca. 1222) are not derived from the saga. A number of parallels have been drawn between *Viga-Glums saga* and other sagas, but some of these are dubious, and in all but one of them *Viga-Glums saga* is most likely the original, or both are descended from common originals now lost, or they make use of stereotyped motifs. The exception is *Egils saga* (written ca. 1220–30),[5] which resembles *Viga-Glums saga* in a number of respects. If the author of one saga is bearing in mind the overall design of the other, *Egils saga* must be the original and *Viga-Glums saga* the imitator, for much of *Egils saga* is founded on ancient verse, and its historical view shows a broad grasp which makes *Viga-Glums saga* look provincial by contrast. But the resemblances may be coincidental, and no real conclusion can be based on them.

Comparison with events contemporary with the author sometimes produces more exactly dateable parallels, but has to be cautiously evaluated. One night in 1222 Haf, the bailiff at Hrafnagil in Eyjafjord, whose name means 'Goat', was murdered, and next day a workman there named Gunnar came to the local chieftain, Sighvat Sturluson of Grund, and confessed to the killing. Sighvat made light of it, and his wife Halldora harboured Gunnar until he was drowned at sea shortly afterwards. A workman from Stokkahladir called Jon Birnuson was

---

4. However, see *Einarsbók*, ed. Bjarni Guðnason, Halldór Halldórsson and Jónas Kristjánsson, Reykjavík 1969, pp. 196–204; Jónas Kristjánsson, *Um Fostbræðrasögu*, Reykjavík 1972, pp. 226–7; and ch. 23 note 4 below.

5. For the date of *Egils saga*, see Sigurður Nordal, *Um Íslenzkar Fornsögur*, Reykjavík 1968, pp. 122–5.

now sent by Sighvat to fast at Stafaholt in expiation of sin; as a result, popular suspicion fell on him. But ten years later, at the point of death, Jon denied having killed Haf, and the implication is that Sighvat himself may have been behind the murder.

The correspondences between this story and chs. 13–15 of *Viga-Glums saga* are fairly obvious. If we accept a contemporary allusion here, it follows that the story of Ingolf was composed after the Autumn of 1222, when suspicion began to fall on Jon Birnuson, and most likely immediately after Jon's death in 1232. In that case, since the Ingolf story also uses the saga itself as a source, the saga must have been in existence by that date.

But the story of Ingolf is also indebted to an internationally known parable in which a young man is persuaded by an older one, sometimes his father, to make trial of his supposed friends by seeking refuge with them, claiming to have killed a man of the same name as an animal which he has actually killed. The version which resembles Ingolf's story most closely is in the *Disciplina Clericalis* of Petrus Alphonsi, a converted Jew who lived in 12th-century Spain. It is perhaps unlikely that the interpolator of the saga was using the *Disciplina Clericalis* directly, but he must have had access to some source related to it, most likely a clerical one such as a sermon exemplum, (further see Turville-Petre, Introduction pp. xxxii-xxxviii). The episode is not, therefore, based solely on 13th-century events.

At the battle of Örlygsstadir in 1238 a man from Eyjafjord was saved by his coat of mail, which he called *fulltrúi* ('source of reliance'), the name of the game in ch. 14 of the saga, and when Sighvat Sturluson fell in the same battle, his kinsman Sighvat Runolfsson lay on top of him and was stabbed to death, like Glum's two slaves at the battle of Hrisateig. But these parallels could show the saga itself influencing the lives of those who knew it, or they could be coincidence. The date of the saga is therefore uncertain, but seems most likely to have been about 1230.

Some of its source material must have been oral, most obviously the verses. But these alone, even if all attributed to their supposed authors and placed in a set order, tell us rather little and relate to only a few incidents. The author may also have used early written genealogical material – he sometimes includes genealogical details not relevant to his story as if from a source with a less specific purpose – and this source could also have contained other historical material, though this can only be a guess.

Jónas Kristjánsson suggests in his introduction (pp. XXVII — XXXVI) that one such source was a lost saga about the men of Espihol, *Esphælinga saga*, some of whose contents survive in a late version of *Landnámabók*. He argues convincingly that in an area as small as Eyjafjord the second saga can hardly have been written without knowledge of the first; but if anything, it seems more likely to me that *Viga-Glums saga* was written first. Its author would have found some of the extra detail in *Esphælinga saga* useful, and it seems easier to take the *Esphælinga saga* account of the events of ch. 27 as a correction of *Viga-Glums saga* than the other way round. But the question cannot really be decided.

The author and his audience certainly knew Eyjafjord well, and the saga was most likely written at or near Thvera itself, where a Benedictine monastery had been founded in 1155 and round which the geographical information is most minutely accurate, though the author also knows something of Hörgardal, the area of Glum's exile. He also had a detailed grasp of the law and an interest in poetry and local tradition, and these things would suggest a person of fairly high rank with experience of secular law. But several known 13th-century Icelanders fit this description, and some now unknown may also have done so, so the name of the author can only be guessed at. Whoever he was, he inhabited a turbulent, anxious political world, and his work could hardly remain unaffected by the sombre outlook of the time.

Chronology and Historicity

Until this century most criticism treated the sagas as history, and although nowadays more sceptical views are in fashion, factual proof is often hard to find in either direction. Some of the verses can be linguistically dated almost to within living memory of the events described. Unfortunately, the definitely early ones (vv. 1, 5, 6 and 11) make little overt reference to major events, while the informative verses 9 and 13 cannot be dated. But as no verse is certainly younger than the saga says it is, the burden of proof must rest with those who deny the traditions found in them.

The Icelandic Annals include the slaying of Sigmund (dated 944) and the battle of Hrisateig (dated 983).[6] Glum's forty years of power would thus begin with Thorkel's departure from Thvera in Spring 946; the battle of Hrisateig in Spring 983 would be followed by the first, unsuccessful prosecution in the same year, then by Glum's equivocal oath in Autumn 984, his defeat at the General Assembly in Summer 985, and his departure from Thvera in Spring 986. The end of the saga divides the forty years into two equal periods, in the first of which he was unrivalled in Eyjafjord, while in the second no one was more than his equal. It can be calculated from Ari's Íslendingabók ('Book of the Icelanders') that the division of Iceland into quarters (ca. 962–5) probably involved the creation of new chieftains among Glum's neighbours, one of whom quickly became his equal.[7] The saga therefore seems to contain a roughly accurate historical tradition here, although the author may not have been very interested in exact dates.

For events outside Iceland the saga's chronology inspires less confidence. Eyjolf cannot have visited Norway during Hakon's reign (from ca. 946). If he had gone abroad in 946, he would have returned with Astrid in 951, and Glum could not have been born before 954 or

---

6. See *Islandske Annaler indtil 1578*, ed. G. Storm, Christiania 1888.
7. See *Skímir* CXI, 1937, pp. 67–8.

have killed Sigmund before Autumn 970; the battle of Hrisateig would then have been in 1009, well after his supposed death (ca. 1003). Even substituting the traditional date 933 or 934 for Hakon's accession, Glum could not have been born before 941 or have killed Sigmund until 957. If Eyjolf's visit to Norway ever took place (and it is probably fictitious), it must have been earlier — taking the Annals' date for the slaying of Sigmund, Glum would have been born ca. 928, Eyjolf must have married by 925 and have gone abroad by 920.

In 1938 the grave of a young man was discovered near the spot where Bard is said to have died (ch. 19).[8] Excavation showed that the area was wooded at the time of burial. The skeleton was facing north, suggesting a heathen burial, since christians were always buried facing east. The teeth suggested a healthy man, 25 to 30 years old, but there was no evidence as to the cause of death. With the skeleton were a sword, well made but undecorated, of a common later 10th-century type, and a spearhead, another undecorated but effective weapon, of a rarer Baltic type, from the late 10th or early 11th century.

This burial certainly could be that of Bard — the approximate period and place, the existence of woodland, the man's age at death, and even the forthright, no-nonsense efficiency of the weapons agree with the character and circumstances described by the saga. The only discrepancy is the appearance of sword and spear where the saga mentions sword and shield. This is as good a piece of corroboration as archaeology is likely to produce for a saga incident — but we cannot prove that no other warrior was buried there in the same period, or that the saga has not distorted the story. Much excavation remains to be done in Eyjafjord, but while archaeological excavation may prove a saga account impossible, it can never prove it true, only, at most, that it could be true; to this extent, archaeology is a biased witness.

In the story of Klæng in ch. 27 we have to deal with conflicting

---

8. See Kristján Eldjárn, *Gengið á reka*, Akureyri 1948, pp. 54–62.

traditions. The account derived from *Esphælinga saga* tells how Glum was pushed down the slope, quotes vv. 11 and 12, reports that Glum wounded Einar in the hand, that Einar killed Grim, and that Glum's protegé was outlawed — very much as in *Viga-Glums saga*. But its account of the origins of the feud is very different. The ancestor with whom the story begins is still called Narfi, but is not the same person — *Viga-Glums saga* has probably confused the two. Thorvald of Hagi, the victim in *Viga-Glums saga*, here becomes the murderer, but his wife in *Viga-Glums saga* remains the wife of the victim, this being necessary in order to involve her kinsman Einar on the opposite side to Glum. The historical murderer was probably Thorvald, as in *Esphælinga saga*, for, as Glum was in fact unrelated to Narfi of Hrisey, there would be no reason for him to defend Narfi's son Klæng.

Some other elements must be historically untrue. The last paragraph claims that Glum was confirmed during his final illness by Bishop Kol, who probably came to Iceland ca. 1025, long after Glum's death. The content of Eyjolf's adventures with the bear and the berserk in chs. 3 and 4 and Glum's parallel attack on a berserk called Björn ('Bear') in ch. 6 are the stuff of a great deal of romantic and legendary saga material, although they are not treated in a conventional way. The Ingolf story is also probably fictitious (unless it alludes to 13th-century events), and that of Skuta is geographically impossible as told here.

That Glum and his major associates and opponents did live and hold power in the 10th century, there can be no doubt. It seems likely that he was born about 928, killed Sigmund about 944, and fought at Hrisateig about 983, losing his lands at Thvera by 986, and dying about 1003. He may have composed some or all of the verses attributed to him, and his son Vigfus, certainly a warrior, could have killed Bard ca. 976–7. But this is a bald summary — the saga remains essentially the imaginative product of a gifted literary artist.

The Genealogy, the Law, and the Verses

These three aspects of any saga are likely to seem particularly alien to the modern reader, and a brief comment on each of them in *Viga-Glums saga* seems desirable.

Modern readers often expect a novel to offer the psychological biography of an individual, or at most a small group of individuals, and to this expectation the use of genealogy is at best an irrelevance and at worst may infect the tale with an unmanageably large cast of characters and an absence of focus on any of them. By this view, most of the best known sagas are seriously deficient — *Egils saga*, for example, does not even introduce its titular hero until 30 of its 87 chapters are complete. But if we regard a saga as the biography of a family or locality, with recurring characteristics to be seen in a succession of characters, whose actions have consequences spanning several generations, this objection disappears; a certain amount of genealogy becomes necessary for the orientation of the reader.

Genealogy is also appropriate because of the indebtedness of sagas to historical writing. As Iceland was a republic, ownership of land did not depend on royal grant, as elsewhere in Europe, but on descent or purchase from the family of the original settler of that land, and genealogy therefore acquired great social and historical importance. A glance at *Landnámabók* ('The Book of Settlements') shows this importance in the writing of history, and if the saga writer wished to recreate the objective appearance of historical fact, he could hardly expect to be believed unless he made use of the same sort of genealogical apparatus.

Finally, genealogy can be used as a 'placing' device. Often the people named in it include some who were famous to the audience (the mention of King Olaf Tryggvason in *Viga-Glums saga* ch. 5 is an obvious example). The use of well-known names can function as a further assurance that the story being told is historically reliable — whether it really is or not — and perhaps also that the real, everyday world continues to exist all around the concerns of the central characters.

But genealogy may be well or badly integrated into the construction of a saga. The ideal of skill and tact is probably *Njáls saga*, where the motivation of genealogy to the tale is handled at chapter openings with great skill (see for example chs. 19, 20 and 26). *Viga-Glums saga* adopts the different strategy of grouping all the genealogical material in a few large blocks (see the first half of ch. 5, most of ch. 10, and the openings of chs. 17 and 27), with rather variable success. All four passages make use of balance, in which the families of two parties who are opponents (or soon to become so) are outlined, but while this works well in setting up the oppositions between Vigfus and Bard in ch. 17 and between Klæng and Thorvald in ch. 27, chs. 5 and 10 are less successful. In the first case, a brief description of Eyjolf's return to Iceland and of Glum's adolescence has to be combined with the genealogy, which is itself too complex and compressed to be easily followed. In ch. 10 there is the common theme of the wives married by Glum and the men of Espihol, but the balance is not wholly successful because of the introduction of Gizur and his daughters, which turns out to be a different sort of material. But these are minor blemishes, and their complexity may be due largely to the abbreviation of the saga carried out by the editor of the M. version.

Like many other sagas of Icelanders, *Viga-Glums saga* is concerned with power struggles within the law, but this does not imply the administration of moral or social justice — rather an amoral contest between powerful men, for the idea of a duty to honour the law for its own sake was alien to Old Icelandic culture, at least in usual practice. The exact law of 10th-century Iceland is not known, and apart from a few traditions was probably not known to the saga writer either; except where otherwise stated, the law for the characters in his story is apparently assumed to have been, as in his own day, that embodied in the code of law known as *Grágás* ('The Grey Goose').[9]

Legal and political power in the Icelandic republic rested with the 39 hereditary chieftains, originally heathen priests, who made up the lawgiving governing body of the General Assembly, each of whom was responsible for the security of his own supporters. About 962–5, the country was divided into quarters, each with three local Assemblies (except that the Northern quarter had four) which, along with quarter Assemblies, dealt with disputes between local people and were presided over in rotation by the three chieftains attached to each. The chieftaincy held by Glum's family was one of the three attached to Vadlathing, the local Assembly for Eyjafjord.

The General Assembly acted both as parliament and supreme court. Founded in 930, it remained independent until its submission to the Norwegian crown in 1262–4; in the 10th century, it opened on the Thursday which began the tenth week of Summer (between the 11th and 17th of June) and lasted for two weeks. Its governing body was presided over the Law-Speaker, the only paid servant of the state, who also gave judgement on points of law and recited the law aloud (until it was written down, early in the 12th century). The local and quarter Assemblies, which could last up to a week, were held between the fifth and seventh weeks of Summer. There were also public meetings of the local Assemblies in mid July, lasting for one or two days, whose main business was the announcement of the enactments of the preceding General Assembly and of the calendar for the coming year. Inauguration of the local Assembly and of the July meeting was a legal requirement on the presiding chieftain.

Anyone bringing a prosecution had first to deliver a summons, at the defendant's home and in the presence of witnesses, two weeks before a

---

9. *Grágás I–III*, ed. Vilhjálmur Finsen, Copenhagen 1852–83; *Laws of Early Iceland-Grágás I*, trans. Andrew Dennis, Peter Foote, Richard Perkins, University of Manitoba, Winnipeg 1980 (two further volumes expected), see pp. 239–62.

local Assembly or four weeks before the General Assembly; the dead might be prosecuted as well as the living, and in heathen times a dead man being summonsed probably had to be exhumed (see ch. 9). The verdict at Local Assemblies was usually 'a verdict of one's neighbours', but with crimes where circumstantial evidence rather than agreed fact was likely to be decisive the case was decided by 'a verdict of twelve' — see ch. 17 — twelve householders or freedmen nominated and led by the presiding chieftain, who was in practice often able to obtain whatever result he wanted.

The court could sentence a man to 'greater' or 'lesser' outlawry. Lesser outlawry involved a payment to one's chieftain in return for up to three years' grace within which to arrange a passage into exile, where one had to remain for another three years before being able to return as a free man. Between sentence and exile, one was allowed sanctuary in three places and on and within bowshot range of the roads between them. Failure to comply with all the conditions transformed a man into a full outlaw, whose property was forfeit, who could be killed wherever he was found, and whom it was an offence to harbour, protect or convey out of the country. There was no legal sanctuary for outlaws in churches, and in heathen times it was apparently thought particularly heinous to harbour a full outlaw in a cult-place — see ch. 19, where the tradition may be derived from *Egils saga*.[10]

Outlawry could not normally take effect before a court of confiscation had been held by the plaintiff and his supporters, fourteen days after the end of the convicting assembly, between dawn and midday, at the convict's residence. This could be expensive for the plaintiff, who had to pay all incidental expenses and settle the outlaw's debts, provide for his dependants, allow his wife her own property, and give a cow or a four-year-old ox to his own chieftain. After that, he received half the outlaw's remaining property, the other half going to

---

10. See Ólafur Briem, *Heiðinn Siður á Íslandi*, Reykjavík 1945, pp. 132–3.

the community for the upkeep of indigent relatives of the outlaw.[11] This provided for innocent relatives and gave the plaintiff an incentive to agree a settlement at an earlier stage.

Out-of-court settlements were common, since all legal actions were brought by one private individual against another. They seem to have been of three major types: agreements to limit the number of actions brought, agreed compensations, and agreed penalties or the removal of them. Compensation could be agreed between the parties, their negotiating friends or relatives (as in *Viga-Glums saga* chs. 9 and 26), by independent arbitrators (see *Njáls saga* ch. 56), or stipulated by the injured party alone — this last usually when no legal defence could be offered (as in ch. 18), but sometimes as an instrument of oppression (see ch. 7). Chapter 14 of *Viga-Glums saga* contains an unusual case of the defendant alone deciding the compensation, but this is fictitious and improbable. The simplest agreed penalty was prosecution on a lesser charge in return for payment (see ch. 19). Also common in the sagas (though never mentioned in *Grágás*) is local outlawry, whereby the victim is banned from a defined area but suffers no court of confiscation (see ch. 26). Alternatively, a defendant might be required to swear his innocence with a legally binding oath, on pain of a fine and resumption of the prosecution (see ch. 25); the discovery of a false oath could be followed by full outlawry.

Occasionally, violent action without process of law might be legally justified. After any killing, rape or concealed theft, and some cases of serious assault, public slander and adultery, summary revenge was legal if taken by the injured party or his closest relatives within 24 hours and at the same place. Any killer was legally bound to announce his crime within three days at the nearest safe place, and at all events before five of the nine nearest householders; the crime was then usually

---

11. Luðvík Ingvarsson, *Refsingar á Íslandi á þjóðveldistímanum*, Reykjavík 1970, pp. 107–8; *Laws of Early Iceland* pp. 90–1.

manslaughter (*víg*). But if he failed to announce it in this way, concealed the body, or had killed unfairly, the crime was murder (*morð*); this outlawed him by virtue of the deed itself — subsequent legal proceedings were merely recognition of it. If he were then killed before conviction at an Assembly, that conviction retrospectively exonerated his killer (see chs. 8–9), and he remained an outlaw even if the court of confiscation was not held (see ch. 27).

The author of *Viga-Glums saga* shows a detailed grasp of the law, produces some points for legal discussion, sometimes comes near to direct quotation of *Grágás*, and has some antiquarian legal knowledge.[12] In the interpolated Ingolf episode (chs. 13–15), however, we find a different picture. Here Glum carries out a killing and makes sure that Ingolf is prosecuted for it. When he announces the true facts of the case, he has not acknowledged the slaying as the law demands, and the Espihol men could have refused the small compensation offered and prepared a murder charge against Glum himself. The story does not stand up in legal terms — its point lies rather in wordplay and moral exemplum, and it uses the law merely as cardboard scenery.

Skaldic verse, of which the earliest surviving examples date from the middle of the 9th century, was still being composed when the sagas were written in the 13th. A full verse consists of eight three-stress lines, each with six syllables; in *dróttkvætt*, the metre found in *Viga-Glums saga*, two of the stresses in each odd-numbered line alliterate with the first

---

12. One point for discussion is Glum's successful contention that the killing of Sigmund was legally justified, which turns on the fine point of whether Sigmund's extortion of the field amounts to concealed theft; Astrid's 'I'll either have what is mine or do without' (ch. 7) echoes the beginning of the law of property in *Grágás* Ib, ch. 227, p. 162; and antiquarian legal details include the exhuming of a dead defendant to serve a summons on him (ch. 9), the taking of oaths on a sacred ring (ch. 25 and note 2), and the hallowing of boundaries with fire (ch. 26 and note 4).

stress of the following line, and there is consonance (i.e. a different vowel followed by the same consonant(s)) between two of the stressed syllables in each odd-numbered line, and full rhyme between two stressed syllables in each even-numbered line. Adherence to this demanding metre was only possible because Icelandic is a highly inflected language, with the grammatical function of each word shown by distinctive forms rather than by position as in English. The poet could therefore arrange his utterance in almost any word order, though it was usual for the two halves of a stanza each to be self-contained. Complexity was further increased by elaborate conventional metaphors ('kennings'), often alluding to heathen mythology and comprehensible only with reference to it, and frequently compounded with each other to describe one object. The result was a kind of poetry which most modern taste finds difficult to enjoy, and whose inclusion in so many sagas may seem puzzling.

Thirteenth-century writers themselves sometimes regard skaldic verses as a historical source. Verses were almost impossible to alter materially without obvious corruption of sense or metre, and most are traditionally attributed to named poets composing about contemporary events. In the prologue to his *Heimskringla* (the history of the kings of Norway), Snorri Sturluson says:

> ... and we pay the greatest attention to what is said in the poems which were recited before the chiefs themselves or their sons. We take as true everything to be found in these poems about their journeys or battles. For although it is the practice of poets to praise most highly the man in whose presence they then are, yet no one would dare to attribute to a man in his presence deeds which all who were listening, including himself, knew to be deception and falsehood. That would be mockery, not praise.[13]

---

13. Snorri Sturluson, *Heimskringla* I, ed. Bjarni Aðalbjarnarson, *Íslenzk fornrit* XXVI, Reykjavík 1941, Prologus, p. 5; the translation is mine.

This is sensible as far as it goes, but verses might be fabricated at a later date and attributed to poets long dead; and Snorri is talking about poems in praise of kings and chieftains, while occasional verses like those in *Viga-Glums saga* often express only personal feelings.

But small differences can sometimes be seen between the skaldic poetry of different periods.[14] Linguistic evidence shows vv. 1, 5, 6 and 11 of *Viga-Glums saga* to be probably from the 11th century or earlier; vv. 3, 7 and 10 seem to date from the mid 12th century or before; and to this category we may add vv. 8 and 12, which are quoted and attributed to Glum by Snorri. For vv. 2, 4, 9 and 13 there is no evidence, but v. 4 is part of a sequence (vv. 4–6) of which the other two are ancient. We cannot, of course, assert that the verses were composed by the people to whom they are attributed, but it seems unlikely that any of them are by the saga author.

But these occasional verses do not for the most part corroborate important historical events, as in *Heimskringla*, or hold the story together, as in *Gisla saga* and perhaps *Kormáks saga*. They are not even part of the biography of a famous poet, as in *Egils saga*, for Glum's verses are few. Their use is more probably due to the laconic style of the sagas, which observes men, words and actions from the outside. This respects the reader's intelligence by not coercing his reactions (though it may covertly persuade), and gains conviction by not requiring an unrealistically omniscient narrator. But it also makes it difficult to portray emotions, particularly in a society in which reticence was considered a virtue; and the use of skaldic verse is a way round this difficulty. It separates itself firmly from the prose round it, so that the emotions in it are contained within it. Its obscurity is a defence against

---

14. For tests of age, see Einar Ó. Sveinsson in *The Saga-Book of the Viking Society*, vol. XVII part 1, pp. 28–35, and Peter Foote's tailpiece essay in George Johnston's *The Saga of Gisli*, London 1963, pp. 112–23. A good introduction to this kind of verse is E.O.G. Turville-Petre *Scaldic Poetry*, Oxford 1976, which includes brief analyses of vv. 1, 2 and 8 of *Viga-Glums saga* (pp. 56–9).

suspicions of over-expressive behaviour, and it does not violate the realistic convention of the saga as a whole.

All the verses in *Viga-Glums saga* have an emotional mainspring (except the probably spurious quatrain 3). The sombre force of Glum's reaction in v.1 (ch. 7) heightens tension before the slaying of Sigmund. Verses 4–6 (ch. 21), expressing Glum's dreams of foreboding, have a similar function leading up to the battle at Hrisateig. Verse 7 (ch. 23) is an important element in the plot. Verses 8 and 9 (ch. 26) dramatise Glum's feelings as he is turned away from his farm, and have a sad dignity. Verses 10–12 (ch. 27) represent the differing reactions of three men to the sudden violence at the Local Assembly — Brusi 'the poet' shows technical skill combined with a certain detachment, Einar's verse is full of excitement and blunt force, with its repeated sea-king kennings, while Glum's is in two halves, the first focusing on the hesitancy of Einar's men, the second on the heroic preparedness of his own. Glum's last verse (v. 13) is a moving lament for lost strength and power, but also has a dramatic role, lulling us into the belief that his active life is over before his last surprise attempt to settle old scores.

There remains v.2, which Glum recites after his dream of his grandfather's personal spirit. Turville-Petre (p. 64) gives an accurate prose 'decoding' of it:

> I saw a woman spirit of towering stature, a goddess of the head-dress, walk hither to Eyjafjǫrðr, with a helmet on her head. So that in my dream the battle-goddess seemed to stand beside the hills, warrior.

If we retain natural prose order but put the kennings back in, we get something like:

> I saw the hawk's island's ice's earth, the personal spirit of men, going under helmet in Eyjafjord in great size; so that it seemed to me in my dream that the bow's terror's judgement's felling goddess stood level with the mountains, man who offers the trouble of armies.

25

The 'hawk's island' is the wrist (because of the sport of hawking), and the 'wrist's ice' is silver, whose 'earth' is the woman who wears silver (i.e. bracelets on her wrist), Earth being also a goddess. The 'bow's terror' is probably a sword, whose 'judgement' is battle — the felling battle-goddess being a valkyrie (strictly, the guardian spirit is not a valkyrie, but valkyrie kennings are a common circumlocution for 'woman'). The utterance now begins to seem more like poetry, but we have still not placed the images in their proper order. Disregarding overall sense, one could do this as follows:

> To go I saw of the island under helmet
> of hawk in great size,
> Earth, in Eyjafjord
> of ice, of men the personal spirit,
> then so that of judgement in dream
> bow's terror to me seemed
> felling goddess with the fells,
> army-trouble's offerer, to stand.

To this we must add an important pun — *dals* ('bow's'), the first word of line 6, is also the genitive singular of *dalr* ('valley'). We now have a more coherent series of images, with effective contrast of movement/rest between the first word and the last, and persistent concentration on images of land throughout the stanza. This is in accordance with Snorri's advice — 'Metaphors are thought to be well composed if the image taken up is sustained through the whole length of the verse' (*Háttatal* ch. 1) — but the image here is central to Glum's concerns. For him, advancement is equivalent to the control of land, and he has recently killed Sigmund for trying to deprive him of his best field. His obsession with the estate to which he is entitled is central to the understanding of the whole story — the malice of Thorkel the Tall's prayer, Glum's concentrated and amoral defence of his interests, and the pathos of his final separation from his lands. There are similar 'land' images in others of Glum's verses (see vv. 1, 3, 4, 6, 8 and 9, and see ch. 26 note 5 below), but nowhere as many as here, where the understanding of the whole saga is affected by the emotion of the verse. The important emotional impact of a verse is here (and usually) contained more in imagery than in literal sense, and the images usually only stand out clearly in the order in which the poet has placed them. I have therefore tried to retain this order as far as possible, even at the cost of a loss of brevity. The exceptions are the two half-verses (v.3 in *Viga-Glums saga* and the verse in *The Tale of Thorvald Chatterbox*), which are in the same metre, but are little more than satirical doggerel and have no complicated imagery.

Structure, style and characterisation

It is important to remember that the sagas were intended to be read aloud, so that the majority of those who first experienced *Viga-Glums saga* would do so by hearing it, and this fact influences the structure of the saga as well as its style and methods of characterisation.

The transience of oral performance dictates first, that the saga should have a clear overall shape which the listener can recognise and remember; second, that the structure should flow logically and without episodes irrelevant to the main theme; and finally, it is desirable that the action should include more detailed patterns and repetitions, allowing the listener to relate one episode to another, though these must not be too obtrusive, or they will undermine the saga's credibility as 'history'. Frequent variation of content, mood and style, and between speech and narrative, is also needed to keep the interest of a listening audience.

The structure of *Viga-Glums saga* is at first sight disconcerting. After raising expectations of the biography of an admirable hero, with early exploits abroad and the apparently heroic defeat of tyrannical opponents, it disappoints us. It emerges instead as the story of a man who rejects heroic ethics, and perhaps all other ideals as well, and who

27

finally pays the penalty. If we expect to be able to identify with the hero, our hopes will not be fulfilled; it is only in the light of Glum's own sardonic detachment from everything but self-interest that the shape of the saga can be enjoyed.

The saga begins with the adventures of Glum's father (chs. 1–4), treated like slightly off-key folktale. Eyjolf is the man for whom everything is too easy to be real — his father's irrational prejudice against foreigners is overcome by a single generous gesture; his friend's brother Ivar, supposedly a villainous bloodthirsty viking, turns out to be a gentleman at heart; conveniently, a bear turns up at the vital moment so that Eyjolf can impress Ivar — but only a small one, which is not too difficult either to track or to kill. Eyjolf takes on himself a duel against the fearsome berserk Asgaut, but after all the suspense of the preliminaries he defeats him with a single blow — not cleaving his skull in the heroic manner of Skarphedinn in *Njáls saga*, but rather tamely slicing his foot off.[15] Finally, he departs for home with the statutory beautiful princess as a bride and predictions of a great future, begets the necessary characters for the story to continue — and dies forthwith.

To some extent, the touches of ridicule in the first four chapters may be to prevent Glum from being outshone by his father, for the next section (chs. 5–6) shows the son going abroad on a parallel adventure. But the son is not the folktale hero, rather an unromantic realist. He too has to impress the high-born foreigner, killing a berserk called Björn ('Bear') to parallel his father's bear and berserk, but his attitude and methods are different. Where Eyjolf seeks out a fight and makes heroic speeches before fighting his berserk formally with sword and shield, Glum waits until the berserk annoys him personally, and then tells him

---

15. It is possible, however, that this was a traditional narrative detail, since it is also found in *Ketils saga Hœngs* ch. 4 and, in a less similar form, in *Eyrbyggja saga* ch. 8. In all three cases the person whose leg or foot is wounded or cut off is clearly in the wrong.

he's a fool and belabours him with a log. Where the Eyjolf episode takes the pretensions of the Norwegians to splendour and nobility at their face value, like any folktale, the Glum adventure sees the magnificence as hollow and Vigfus as a rather shallow temporiser who is impressed by strength and violence rather than by a just claim on him, and whose offer of power and position does not have to be taken seriously compared with what has to be done at home (even if Glum, to further his own prestige, is quite prepared later to exaggerate Vigfus's honour and splendour — see ch. 9).

In the next section (chs. 7–10), Glum turns from the attempt at fairy-tale success to practical assertion of his rights. As in the preceding chapters, the reader's sympathies are bound to be with him at first — he is the young hero for whom the folktale stereotype demands our allegiance, and he has besides a just cause. But his arrogance and brutality try our loyalty at several points. Chapter 7 contradicts the stereotype by acknowledging that events do not stand still in the real world while the folktale hero is on his adventures abroad, and sets up the incident with Sigmund's cattle as a foretaste. It begins with Astrid waking Glum up, a motif repeated in a leisurely way in ch.8, which may lead us to expect another warning action; instead, we hear of the sudden killing of Sigmund, not in romantic 'fair fight', but by a calculating attack that gives him no chance of defending himself; and Thorstein's worries are treated with the same muted contempt by Glum as by Astrid in ch. 7. Chapter 9 shows Glum to be as determined in the legal proceedings as in the killing, and it also sets up the major antagonism of the rest of the saga, Glum's ruthlessness against the pushing of the well-meaning Thorarin by his pugnacious relatives. Glum's self-assertion as the leading man of his area is completed by his marriage in ch. 10.

So far, the message of the narrative seems to be that hard, self-interested realism is what pays, but the next section (chs. 11–12 and 17–19, omitting the interpolated chapters) deals with the effects of Glum's rise to power on his supporters and opponents. Glum's

29

advantageous marriage leads Arnor Red Cheek also to aspire to an ambitious match, and Glum, to keep his own prestige, is forced to support Arnor. Inevitably, this offends another suitor, one of the Espihol men, and although the crisis is averted by Glum's domineering influence, and the affection of the foster brothers results, the prophecy of Oddbjörg lets us know that this is only a patching-up, and that more trouble lies ahead.

And power in Glum's hands encourages not only the ambitious among his men, but also the unscrupulous. Hallvard thinks he can use Glum's patronage as a cloak for theft, and is made safer by his association with Vigfus, the one of Glum's sons who will help to destroy his dynastic hopes at Thvera precisely because he has inherited the qualities of self-seeking determination and suddenness which brought his father to power. The death of Hallvard and Vigfus's revenge against Bard are thus the natural consequences of Glum's own character and power, despite the pragmatic attempts he makes to moderate their effects, first by his settlement with Halli (ch. 18) and then by his attempts to mitigate the penalty for Vigfus's crime (ch. 19). The very success of Glum's hard self-assertion in early life begins now to conspire against him, for the father's lack of consideration for others is taken to its logical conclusion in the son's disregard for legal justice. And yet it is clear that Glum likes the rash, troublesome and selfish Vigfus better than the loyal, cautious and useful Mar. Apart from the dream sequence before the Battle of Hrisateig, where Mar is no more than a convenient audience, Glum speaks once to each of his sons, welcoming Vigfus to the battle with obvious pleasure (while protecting the secret of his identity) and sniping unfairly at Mar's dressing of his wounds afterwards. It is Vigfus, not Mar, in whom Glum recognises his own nature. The final effect of this section, despite the settlement, is to line up with Glum's opponents the one sort of man they lack, who can equal Glum's own calculating determination — Einar. And he who lives by self-interest can have no complaint when he meets an opponent with the same creed.

Glum's enemies now have the two things they need to bring him down — an ally as cunning as he is and a pretext situation, in the relationship between Arngrim and Steinolf. Chapters 20–26 show the stages leading to Glum's fall. In the first of these (ch. 20 and the first half of ch. 21), Einar's calculation and Thorvald Hook's malice work on the natural flaws in the foster brothers to make one kill the other; in this section, Glum suspects that some trickery is afoot, but is too remote in Steinolf's trust to be able to prevent it.

With a crisis duly provoked by Steinolf's death, Glum sends Mar to start legal proceedings (ch. 21), but we are shown in vv. 4–6 that his mind, typically, is running on violent confrontation. In ch. 22 the gratuitously malicious Thorvard is introduced, and his interference at first looks like mere chance; but Glum would hardly tell such a man what he was doing out of pure carelessness. Temporarily denuding himself of men and taking care that Thorvard knows he has done so, with the fair certainty that Thorvard will tell the Espihol men, looks like a calculated risk taken with the aim of provoking a battle. The obvious reaction of the more quarrelsome Espihol men, on being told that Mar is summonsing Arngrim, will be to go out to deliver a counter summons, and some of them will not be averse to a fight. That by itself will not bring the two sides together, but Glum relies on Thorvard's mischief-making to keep him informed of what the Espihol men are doing, and on his cowardice to send his son rather than coming himself. Glum takes full advantage of this 'extra trump' in his hand after the battle (ch. 23) to turn his opponents' legal attack away from himself. But he also loses a vital card in the legal settlement after the battle through the selfishness of Vigfus, whose pardon has to be bought in exchange for the slaying of Steinolf. If Vigfus had complied with the terms of the settlement after the death of Bard, he would have been legally free by the time of the Battle of Hrisateig, Glum would then have been able to set Steinolf's death against that of Thorvald Hook, there would have been no need for the deception involving Gudbrand,

and the case would have ended there.

Nonetheless, Glum's own assertiveness in reciting a foolishly boastful verse is the immediate cause of the reopened case which ultimately brings his downfall, and chs. 24–26 show a cunning rearguard action in which he reveals a contempt for the law as great as that of Vigfus in an attempt to stave off his ultimate defeat. But at last he runs out of strategems in the face of Thorvard's cunning and Einar's grasping persistence, and even the pleasure of spiting Einar by hanging his men is denied to him.

The last chapter is a sort of coda, not thematically irrelevant but rather a demonstration of how Glum's nature impels him to seek revenge. The altered power situation is against him, but his unalterable resolve confers on him a kind of dignity which his manoeuvrings while still in power did not allow him. This chapter thus represents a qualification to the author's view of the anti-heroic attitude. It may carry within itself the seeds of its downfall, he suggests, but when consistently pursued it can command respect. However, the saga ends problematically, with the apparently unlikely account of Glum's deathbed confirmation as a Christian. This has often been regarded as a serious artistic mistake or even as a later addition; but it is in fact a literary convention, found also at the end of *The Tale of Thorvald Chatterbox* and elsewhere (eg. *Vatnsdæla saga* ch. 46, *Bárðar saga Snæfellsáss* ch. 21). Here, the convention is used to give what looks like one last, cold-eyed observation of a protagonist, self-interested to the last, taking out a last-minute insurance for the world to come.

The theme is thus coherently pursued throughout; the minor parallels which support the overall design are too numerous to discuss in detail, but those which compare Eyjolf and Glum have already been noted; one might add small details like the motif of a dark foggy morning before Bard is killed and again before the Battle of Hrisateig, and the parallel between the terms on which Thorkel the Tall and Glum are forced to leave Thvera. A full list of such parallels has been compiled by Régis

Boyer in the introduction to his translation of the saga into French.[16]

In the version of the saga found in M., stylistic repetition is used sparingly and usually for good reasons — sometimes simply to emphasise an important point, like the injustice of Sigmund and Thorkel's behaviour in chs. 7 and 8:

'...she was supposed to have the field if justice had been done.'
'That summer he and his mother should have had the field if justice had been done.'
'...seeing they have the field that we ought to have by rights.'

This is unobtrusively managed, with the repetition in a different context each time, but not all repetitions are so successful: in ch. 23 the regret of the prosecutors on hearing that the killing of Thorvald Hook has been attributed to Gudbrand is rather clumsily repeated, and the legal requirement on Glum to take his oath (ch. 24) is obtrusively re-stated.

More often, the author uses repetition to promote suspense or characterisation. The first can be seen in ch. 22, where Thorarin's repeated instruction to his recalcitrant men to keep riding heightens our instinct that they will disobey him and a battle will result — though the author cleverly appears to defeat our expectations by making it seem that Thorarin has been obeyed after all — but slowly, so that the battle happens anyway. The best examples of repetition used to promote characterisation are in Bard's fatal expedition (ch. 19). Bard's servant repeats that there would be no disgrace in avoiding Vigfus, and, by repeating a point not even mentioned before, reveals his argument as special pleading and helps, despite himself, to point out to Bard why he cannot honourably follow the servant's advice. Next, Bard's repeated mention of the relative numbers suggests that he is trying to convince

---

16. *Trois Sagas Islandaises du XIIIe Siècle et un "Thattr"*, Paris 1964, pp. 39–41.

himself that Vigfus won't attack him unfairly, as if he is not sure; and our suspicions are heightened when Vigfus closes the subject ominously: 'Vigfus told them to wait and see first how things went.'

Variations of style, content and mood are also well handled. The variations in mood may sometimes seem surprising, as when Bard sets off to institute legal proceedings against Hallvard (ch. 18):

> Bard took on the case and went to serve the summons. And when he met Hallvard he brought his case to a prompt conclusion by chopping his head off. Afterwards he told his father.

The sudden change reflects the action, and simultaneously makes us laugh and thereby unconsciously accept that the killing of someone like Hallvard is not a very serious matter. Before we have time to notice how we have absorbed this assumption, we are shown Bard's rashness and his slightly contemptuous attitude of 'do what needs doing first, and tell the old man when it's too late to change it'. Such reliance on black comedy is common, but occasionally a different sort of change can be seen, as in ch. 27, where Glum's response to the cautious voices suggesting that he should not go to the Autumn Assembly transcends the pragmatic struggling of most of the saga by referring to larger, more impersonal and less sordid concerns for civic responsibility.

Modification of style is usually, and rightly, less noticeable; if it were too obtrusive it would be a distraction and thus a flaw. In ch. 9 the legal proceedings at the General Assembly are described in balanced, shapely sentences with a large number of subordinate clauses, giving an effect of a measured, dignified decisiveness. By contrast, where the weakness of Thorarin's authority is being shown (ch. 22), it is marked, despite the good sense of what he says, by his repeated use of the subjunctive and of verbs which indicate that what he says is only his own opinion:

> 'We think it's an awkward matter, offering any settlement to Glum.'
> 'I'd think it a bad thing to proceed with a charge like that.'

'I wouldn't be sure about that being a good plan.'
'This seems ill-advised to me.'

There is no need to emphasise Thorarin's limitation further — the style of his speech is enough to do so by itself. Elsewhere, a sudden stylistic shift can create a special effect, as in ch. 27, where Einar's measured speech before the abortive court of confiscation is followed by a sudden breathless flurry of six principal clauses linked only by 'and', right to the end of the incident, which perfectly expresses the sudden, hectic, disorganised chase being described.

In so naturalistic a genre as the saga, unifying devices have to be treated with caution. Linking by means of symbols, which in most of the imaginative literature of late medieval Western Europe could be used with little constraint because of the unrealistic genres in fashion at the time, would disrupt the audience's view of a saga as history unless they could believe in its literal reality as well as its symbolic meaning. *Viga-Glums saga* contains few but effective reminders of what has preceded, as where, in Glum's dream before his expulsion from Thvera (ch. 26), 'Frey answers shortly and angrily, and remembers now Thorkel the Tall's gift of an ox.' Here the reference back has, because of its supernatural nature, to be placed in a dream to protect its literal credibility. A more truly symbolic link, but still embodied in literal objects, is his grandfather's gift to Glum of a cloak, spear and sword (ch. 6 and see note 1). The sword may be a scribal interpolation, for it is thereafter forgotten, but the cloak and spear are undoubtedly associated with the cult of Odin. We see them again when Glum sets off to kill Sigmund in ch. 8, and when Thorstein recognises them as signs of trouble after Sigmund is dead. Then we forget them until after Glum's oath (ch. 25), when he gives them away — an ordinary social convention, for the giving of gifts at parting is common in the sagas. Only the subtle Einar reminds us, at the end of the chapter, of Vigfus's warning to Glum that he must not part with them. Again, literal realism is protected, for the author states no belief in the powers of the object — we are free to believe that Einar is merely being superstitious if we like. And even that superstition can be motivated as wish fulfillment, for beneath it lies Einar's calculating greed. After reminding us of Vigfus's words, he adds: 'Now I'll take up the case and follow it through.'

This last quotation is also an example of a 'cliff-hanging' chapter ending, but not the only one — another is the suddenly chilling end of ch. 7: 'And he was often affected in this way afterwards, when the mood to kill was on him.' The ends of chs. 12, 13 and 21 function in the same way, and it is noticeable that, apart from the interpolated ch. 13, these fall at fairly regular intervals, suggesting that the author may have been allowing for short breaks in reading, like the intervals in a play, by providing suitable points at which the reader might pause — but this is of course only a guess.

When we turn to methods of characterisation, the first factor introduced by oral performance is the presence of the narrating author or performer. In much European medieval literature this presence is overt, and a Chrétien, a Dante or a Chaucer could make brilliant use of it. But in the sagas great care is taken to conceal it in the fiction that what is being said is objective history — narrated fact dominates to the almost total exclusion even of such comment as we legitimately expect in a real historian.[17] Pronouncements about character are usually in generalised conventional terms:

'...a duellist and quarrelsome.'

---

17. Icelandic historians contemporary with the saga writers were not so averse to subjective comment — thus Abbot Karl Jónsson's *Sverris saga* compares its hero with the young David, and parts of *Sturlunga saga* take the side of Bishop Gudmund 'the Good' in a very partisan way; but these writers may have felt themselves absolved from the need for objectivity by the fact that they were describing events still within or nearly within living memory.

'. . .a very boisterous person, an unscrupulous man, of great strength and full of courage.'
'. . .a turbulent and very unscrupulous man and better than anyone at fighting, hasty in speech and inclined to be abusive.'

In fact, these descriptions apply respectively to Thorvald Hook, Vigfus and Bard, but they are almost interchangeable, no more than pointers to the role the character will play. But despite his concealment the narrator is still present to guide the attitudes of the audience, as in the repetitions and shifts of style discussed above. Elsewhere, the narrator can sum up a character with ironic understatement — thus Thorvald is 'not particularly well intentioned' (ch. 22) — or comment through another character, as when Thordis tells her husband: 'This is the doing of cleverer men than you' (ch. 21), and we realise Arngrim's dreadful stupidity. But such narrative guidance is always conveyed either through stylistic device or through conventionalised description, the words of another character, or the view of an authoritative tradition.

Sudden shifts of mood can also be used to hide the tight logical structure of the plot, for although we demand unity, it has to be clothed with the inconsequentiality of everyday life, or we will dismiss it as contrived. This may be why some of the most decisive actions appear to be prompted by no more than a chance word. Glum's decision to kill Sigmund looks like the result of a reproach from Astrid about his laziness on the farm; the elaborate plan to kill Kalf is triggered by Ingolf's tactless answer in a word game; and the killing of Bard is apparently provoked by his silly joke about Vigfus's beard and his rash expedition to the wood. In each case, though, this represents only a context, not a cause. Astrid has told us in ch. 7 that Glum will not submit to indignity at Sigmund's hands. The same is true of Ingolf's answer in the word game — Mar has told Ingolf that revenge will be taken on Kalf, and Glum has an obviously pre-arranged plan. And Vigfus's public defiance of Glum at Hallvard's trial (ch. 18) suggests that he is unlikely to honour any settlement for long. The result is to suggest that the everyday events are only chance in themselves, while the results they produce follow from larger causes which would sooner or later have brought them about anyway.

Another role of the narrating 'voice' is to distract attention from implausible details in the plot. This is rare in *Viga-Glums saga*, the clearest example being where Skuta evades capture by pretending to be a shepherd (ch. 16). Glum's men are all presumably local, yet they do not realise that Skuta is not one of the local shepherds, nor does anyone recognise him, even though he used to be their master's son-in-law. But we do not notice these flaws at the time, because suspense concentrates our attention on the wordplay Skuta employs to avoid giving his name.

The most obvious comparisons between characters are contrasts, like those between Glum's decisiveness and Thorarin's hesitancy; between Thorarin's prudence and the impulsive foolishness of his brother Thorvald Hook; or between the brothers Mar and Vigfus. There are also contrasts between what a character says or assumes and what the same character does. A clear example of this is the behaviour of Astrid. After she has urged forbearance on Glum (ch. 7), we learn almost immediately her real estimate of his character, given in his absence, when she tells Thorkel and Sigmund that he will 'set her case straight'. And when she then urges him to get up and work at the haymaking, she adds a little postscript about Sigmund and Vigdis in the field, in exactly the right way to ensure that he will fulfil her real wishes by taking vengeance. And this shows that the 'political' manipulations in the saga extend even to the closest family relationships.

There are also some comparisons of like with like, the simplest being the consistent balance between Skuta and Glum throughout ch. 16, though one might also cite the parallels between Vigfus and Bard, especially in ch. 17. Some comparisons are more complex. When we first see Glum pitted against Thorkel the Tall it looks like a simple contrast of justified youth against corrupt age. But before Glum's expulsion from Thvera, the price he is paid is equated with that paid by

Thorkel; Glum is now himself a representative of corrupt age, and like Thorkel before him he attempts a gesture of revenge before he leaves. The comparison between Glum and Einar, the opponent who is most like him, is counterpointed by one effective contrast: Glum seeks to resolve his problems by provoking a battle in which he takes great personal risk; although Einar provokes the killing of Steinolf, he is carefully absent when it is done, and is the only major figure who takes no part in the battle.

Another element in the depiction of character is the opinions about a person that are expressed by others. Some of these are accurate summary of the nature of minor characters, like Thordis's condemnation of Arngrim's stupidity (ch. 21) or Halli the Fat's recognition of Thorvard's trouble-making (ch. 22). The first of these also reflects on Thordis herself, for the accuracy of her view of Arngrim contrasts him unfavourably with Steinolf, and this and the passion in her speech suggest that there just might have been some cause for Arngrim's jealousy. But most such opinions are about Glum himself, and these are not all self-evidently true. They can be tested against each other. Thus Thorkel the Tall's insulting estimate in ch. 7 — 'to us you seem the same sort of idiot now as when you went abroad' — is set against Thorarin's — 'you haven't considered what was to be expected of the descendants of a man like Eyjolf' (ch. 8). More complex are the conflicting views of Glum and Vigfus held by Bard and Halli the White. At first (end of ch. 17) Halli thinks Glum will behave justly and Bard does not, Bard being proved right by events; but later (chs. 18–19) Halli correctly realises that the danger from them is not over, while Bard tries, fatally, to laugh it off.

The sum of the results of these devices is no less interesting than the characterisation in a novel, but because it does not rely on a psychologically omniscient author, it may be more open to argument and, perhaps, more convincing. The objective stance is admittedly a device, but it is honestly used to portray realistic characters in credible situations, not gifted with any superhuman strength, intelligence, sensuality, or luck. Its focus is firmly on a hard real world whose major fault is the inability to form unselfish relationships. Glum neither gives nor receives any disinterested generosity at all — even his mother manipulates him in the interests of her family self-esteem. It may not be a pretty picture, but it skilfully tells us the truth about one kind of human nature, and we cannot justifiably ask for anything more.

VIGA-GLUMS SAGA

Characters

1. *In the Prologue*
   Ingjald of Thvera
   Eyjolf 'the Lump', his son

   Hreidar, a Norwegian merchant
   Ivar, a viking, his brother
   Thorstein, their relative

   Vigfus, a Norwegian nobleman
   Astrid, his daughter

   Asgaut ⎱ berserks
   Björn ⎰

2. *Glum's family and supporters*
   Thorstein of Holar ⎫
   Vigfus   ⎪
   GLUM   ⎬ children of Eyjolf and Astrid
   Helga of Laugaland ⎭
   Halldora, Glum's wife
   Mar   ⎫
   Vigfus ⎬ children of Glum and Halldora
   Thorlaug ⎭
   Thorvald Chatterbox, son of Helga

   Arnor Red Cheek of Uppsalir, Glum's cousin
   Steinolf, his son

Ingolf, Glum's foreman
Hallvard of Tjörn, Glum's freedman, foster-father to Vigfus

Klæng of Hrisey, a kinsman of Glum

Gizur the White
Teit, his father ⎱ chieftains, Glum's allies
Asgrim, son of Ellida-Grim ⎰

3. *Glum's opponents*
Thorkel the Tall of Myvatn, father-in-law to Glum's
  brother Vigfus
Sigmund, his son

Thorir of Espihol
Thorarin of Espihol
Thorvald Hook of Grund ⎱ his children
Thorgrim of Mödrufell
Vigdis, wife of Sigmund ⎰
Arngrim, son of Thorgrim, foster-brother of Steinolf
Thordis, his wife

Eirik, a servant of Thorarin
Kalf of Stokkahladir
Thorvald the Manly of Hagi, related by marriage to the
  Espihol men

Viga-Skuta of Myvatn, briefly Glum's son-in-law

Halli the White of Jorunnarstadir, a blind farmer
Brusi the Poet of Torfufell ⎱ his sons
Bard of Skaldsstadir ⎰
Una, Bard's wife

Einar of Saurbær, Halli's foster-son (see ch. 17 note 2)
Gudmund the Powerful, Einar's brother
Hallbera of Hanakamb, their mother

Hlenni the Old of Vidines
Oddkatla, his wife, sister of Una

Thorvard of Kristnes
Gudbrand, his son

4. *Others*
    Gizur of Tjarnir
    Saldis, his wife
    Thordis
    Herthrud their daughters

    Oddbjörg, a travelling fortune teller

    Thorkel of Hamar
    Helga, his daughter
    Thjodolf of Æsustadir, her suitor

    Halli the Fat of Öngulsstadir

    Vikings, Norwegians, serving men, slaves, relatives
    and supporters of both sides, vagrants, a shepherd at Thvera,
    a missionary bishop.

CHAPTER 1

T HERE WAS A man called Ingjald, son of Helgi the Lean;[1] he lived at Thvera in Eyjafjord. He was an early chieftain and a great leader, but very old at the time of this story. He was a married man and had two sons, Steinolf and Eyjolf, capable men and both good looking. Ingjald was self-willed, taciturn, awkward and stubborn. He had little time for merchants, was unwilling to tolerate their arrogance, and if he wanted anything from them he would send someone else for it rather than go himself.

Now one summer a ship came into Eyjafjord; the captain was called Hreidar, a man of good family who had a farm at Voss in Norway and was very daring and popular. Eyjolf Ingjaldsson was at the ship a lot during the summer, and he and Hreidar became great friends. Hreidar told him that he wanted somewhere to stay in Iceland over the winter, and said that from what he'd heard from other people, he would most like it to be with Ingjald. Eyjolf said that his father hadn't made a habit of having people to stay, but that he would see about it.

When he got home, he suggested to his father that he should take the captain in, and said that he thought he was a good chap and of great worth — and he put the matter to him strongly on the captain's behalf.

Ingjald replied: "If you've invited him already, what's the point of arguing about it? I'll agree to foot the bill, but you must accept all the work involved" — and he said he'd never had a foreigner staying with

---

1. Helgi the Lean, the first settler of Eyjafjord. His semi-Christianity and his gift of land to Ingjald are recorded in "The Book of Settlements" (*Landnámabók*).

him before and that he still didn't really want to.

Then Eyjolf said: "He isn't going to be accepted without your consent — but if the man I've invited can't be put up here then I haven't got much say, and you don't want me to have much either."

Ingjald said: "You can have your own way in this — let the captain come here with one other man, and I won't make it awkward for him for your sake; but you must take all the trouble over them, and I'll pay the expense."

He said: "I'm quite satisfied with that."

Next day he went and found Hreidar and told him how things stood; he seemed pleased about it, and duly moved in with his cargo. And before they'd been there very long, Hreidar found out that there was to be a great Yule feast[2] there. Ingjald was polite but distant towards him.

One day Hreidar called Ingjald into the outbuilding that his cargo was in, and he went. Then Hreidar told him to choose whatever he wanted from the cargo. Ingjald said he didn't want any of his property, but that it was good of him to make the offer. Hreidar replied: "All the same, I've thought of something you ought to accept. I've been to some of the best farms here in Eyjafjord, and I haven't seen a household that can compare with this one. But you don't have such good wall hangings[3] that there aren't similar ones on other farms" — and he took out of his chest such good wall hangings that better had never come to Iceland, and gave them to Ingjald. Ingjald thanked him warmly, and now there was an excellent relationship between them.

Later in the winter Eyjolf told Hreidar he would like to go abroad

---

2. The christian audience which first heard the saga would normally have thought of a *jólaveizla* as a Christmas feast, but here, of course, the participants are heathen. It was not a mid-winter feast, since according to the Icelandic calendar, mid-winter was about the middle of January.

3. It was customary for the halls of prosperous farms to be hung with tapestries, at least on special occasions. In ch. 26, Glum contrasts himself on this basis with the peasantry, who would not have such things.

with him in the spring. He replied without enthusiasm. Eyjolf said:
"Why don't you want to take me? Don't you like me?" "Very much",
said he, "but your father wouldn't think much of my payment for his
hospitality if I took away the son who does him so much credit, and I
won't behave ungenerously to him. But if your father agrees, I'll gladly
take you with me — and in that case I'll be very grateful if you'll
come."

Now the merchants got ready to leave, and when they were ready
Eyjolf approached Hreidar again about his journey abroad. Hreidar told
him what he thought about it, saying that he didn't want to act against
the wishes of Ingjald over his journey abroad. Then Eyjolf told his
father about his eagerness to travel, and also about what had passed
between Hreidar and himself. Ingjald said there could be few men like
Hreidar — "and because you've done the right thing in this and he has
proved his worth, I'll agree to your journey, and I think it better that
you should go with him than with someone else."

CHAPTER 2

About Eyjolf[1]

T HEN THEY WENT abroad and reached Norway. Hreidar
made Eyjolf many offers of places where he could stay,
but he wouldn't accept any of them. Hreidar said: "What do you want
arranged for you then?"

He replied: "I don't know."

Then Hreidar said: "Wouldn't you like to go to a king or some other
chieftain? You'll have my support in that" — at that time Hakon the

---

1. The chapter titles in this translation are taken from M.

foster-son of King Athelstan was King of Norway[2] — "It seems to me a good thing to serve such chiefs, for men like you, who are influential and likely to give effective support."

He replied: "I'm hardly fit to serve kings, though it might perhaps suit me — but still, I won't accept that suggestion."

He asked: "What do you want then?"

"Why are you avoiding inviting me to stay with you, because that's what I want?"

"I have little desire to do that," said Hreidar.

Eyjolf asked: "What's the reason for that?"

"I don't care to offer what it would be bad for you to accept, since it seems to me that you deserve nothing but good from me."

"I'm curious about the cause of this."

"Well, now you shall know about it, though telling it will bring me little credit. I have a brother called Ivar. We own the farm and all the property jointly, and we're very fond of each other, but we differ about one thing, namely that he can't stand Icelanders, so that it is unbearable for them there. Every summer he goes on viking raids, and when he comes home, he comes with ten or a dozen men to my house, and everyone there has to do their bidding. They'll all be so nasty to you that it will simply be intolerable for you there."

He said: "I'm curious about how they'll behave, and you won't be to blame if you allow me your hospitality."

Hreidar replied: "I have an obligation to my brother, who brings me

---

2. The scribe of M. carelessly omits "King of Norway". Athelstan, grandson of King Alfred, ruled Wessex and Mercia 924–40; Hakon, generally called his foster-son in Norse sources, ruled Norway from ca. 946 to ca. 961–4. Medieval Icelandic historians dated his accession, and the reign of his father Harald Finehair, about thirteen years too early. (The true dates can be reconstructed from contemporary references to Hakon's displaced predecessor, Eirik Bloodaxe, in the Old English Chronicle between 947 and 954). If this journey to Norway ever took place, it must have been while Harald Finehair was still king — see Introduction pp. 14–15

the best gifts he can get, that we shouldn't become estranged over you
— but I'll take a dim view if they make fun of you and insult you."

"You really do want to avoid having me!" said Eyjolf. "How will he
treat me? He won't attack me, will he?"

"It'll be worse than a fight. He has a lot of vicious men with him;
they'll twist everything you say or do against you."

Eyjolf said: "That's no hardship, if one knows something about it
beforehand. It's silly not to put up with that sort of thing, and I won't be
put off by that."

Hreidar replied: "I've got obligations on both sides — you're my
friend and he's my brother, and I love him very much."

The upshot was that Eyjolf went home with Hreidar to stay at Voss.
And when Ivar was expected home, Eyjolf took to wearing a fur cloak
every day. He was a big man, and always sat beside Hreidar.

CHAPTER 3
About the brothers

NOW IVAR CAME home and everyone went to meet him as
was fitting and welcomed him cheerfully. Then each of
the brothers asked the other for news — and where had Hreidar been
over the winter? He said he had been in Iceland, but then Ivar asked
nothing more — "But that thing beside you," he said, "is it man or
beast? That's a great lump if ever there was one."

Eyjolf replied: "I'm an Icelander, I'm called Eyjolf, and I plan to stay
here over the winter."

"I have a feeling," said Ivar, "that life on this farm may not be
without its little accidents if an Icelander is to stay here."

Hreidar replied: "If you behave badly towards him, so that he can't
put up with it, then it won't do our relationship any good."

"It's bad luck that you ever went to Iceland, if it's to be the cause of our doing the bidding of Icelanders and abandoning our relatives and friends. I don't know why you like visiting that worst of nations; anyway, you needn't tell me any more news."

"It's not like that," said Hreidar. "Actually, there are lots of good chaps there."

Ivar said: "All the same, that snouted bear[1] doesn't look right in the high seat."

But when Ivar saw that his brother set great store by this man, he began to inveigh against Icelanders less than before — "but what can I do but call him 'Lump'?" Eyjolf said he would gladly acknowledge that name, yet everything he did or said, they twisted.

There was a man called Vigfus; he was a nobleman[2] and ruled over Voss. He was the son of Sigurd, the son of Kari the Viking, and had a daughter called Astrid. There was a great friendship between the brothers and Vigfus; they held the Yule feast alternately at each others' homes, and now it was the brothers' turn to prepare for it. Hreidar had arranged everything beforehand, and now he had to go and invite people, and he asked Eyjolf to go with him — "because I have no curiosity about how *they* will behave towards you."

"I'm not feeling well," said Eyjolf, "so I can't go."

---

1. M.'s form *totabalsinn* is meaningless — Turville-Petre emends to *totabassinn* — "snouted bear", and Jónas Kristjánsson (and some 17th and 18th-century paper MSS) to *tötrabassinn* — "shaggy bear". Turville-Petre's is the smaller emendation, and although Jónas' interpretation gives good sense, Davið Erlingsson has argued persuasively that the sense "snouted bear" must be right, since it is the bear's snout that Eyjolf takes home with him at the end of this incident ("Eyjolf has the last laugh: A note on *Viga-Glúms saga*, chs. I-III", *Speculum Norroenum*, ed. Ursula Dronke, Guðrún P. Helgadóttir, Gerd Wolfgang Weber, Hans Bekker-Nielsen, Odense 1981, pp. 85-8).

2. Vigfus is called *hersir*, an exclusively Norwegian title originally used of men who owed political allegiance to no superior; but after the political unification of Norway (ca. 885) it refers to noblemen somewhat below the highest rank of *jarl*.

That evening, when Hreidar had gone and they sat down at table, Ivar's companions said: "Now the Lump is at home and Hreidar isn't. Now we can have all the fun we want."

"We ought now," said Ivar, "to give some thought to how we ought to behave. Here we are, two brothers owning our property jointly, and he bears all the responsibility for it and I none; and here is one man he wants to help, and we behave so that he can hardly tolerate it. But he hasn't done us any harm, so nobody is to slander him while Hreidar is away from home."

They said that now was a good chance to have a bit of fun.

Then Ivar made a speech: "What you're suggesting is not gentlemanly. Everyone waits on us here, and we have every amusement we feel like, while others have the work and the anxiety. And even if this man had killed my brother, I ought not to do him any harm, for Hreidar's sake. No one will be allowed to make fun of him, and he is not to be called Lump any more."

Next morning Ivar said to Eyjolf: "Would you like to come into the forest with us and amuse yourself?" He agreed to that and went with them — they were felling trees for themselves and bringing them home. Eyjolf had a sword and a hatchet. Ivar said: "I advise you, Icelander, if each of us goes off alone, that you get home before dark."

Then each man went his own way in the forest, and Eyjolf went off by himself. He took off his fur cloak and laid his sword, which he had had in his hand, on top of it; and he walked about in the forest amusing himself with his axe by cutting down the trees which appealed to him. But as the day wore on it began to snow. Then he decided to go home and came to where the cloak had lain. It was gone, but the sword was still there. He saw that the snow had been swept away as if the cloak had been dragged along. And in fact a forest bear had come and dragged the cloak away. It had hardly had the strength to hold it up, for it was a young bear, newly out of the lair, and hadn't yet killed anyone. Then he went on and saw the bear sitting in front of him. He drew his sword,

51

struck the snout off the animal at the eyes, and took it home in his hand.

But Ivar came home first, missed Eyjolf and said: "We have behaved unworthily and done wrong in parting from our companion. He is unfamiliar with the forests, and we can expect there to be a good many dangerous animals about. There will be a lot of talk about it if he doesn't come home, considering how we treated him before, and I suggest that we search for him until we find him." But when they got outside the door, there was Eyjolf coming towards them. Ivar greeted him warmly and asked why he was stained with blood — and he showed them what he was holding. Then Ivar said: "I'm afraid you're wounded."

"Don't worry about that, there's nothing wrong with me."

Then Ivar observed: "It's a foolish practice to insult people one doesn't know;[3] he has shown courage in this business which I don't know whether any of us would have equalled."

The next evening Hreidar came home. Ivar said: "Why are you so gloomy, brother? Are you worried about the Lump? What are you expecting me to have done to him?"

Hreidar replied: "How you've treated him will certainly make a difference to us both."

He said: "What will you do now to have me treat him as you do?"

He replied: "I'll give you that gold ring we own in common and that you've long admired."

He said: "I'm not going to get greedy for your inheritance, but from now on I shall behave to him as I do to you yourself, and now he must sit beside me, and not beside you." After that they both treated him with great respect and saw that the place he sat in was well looked after. And so it went on.

---

3. Hermann Pálsson has pointed out ("På Leting etter Røttene til Viga-Glums saga", *Maal og Minne* 1979, pp. 18–26) that versions of this aphorism appear in a number of stories about Icelanders, and may be based on similar advice in such didactic traditional poems as *Hávamál* (see eg. stanza 132).

CHAPTER 4

About the brothers

N OW PEOPLE CAME to the brothers' Yule feast. But when it was arranged to sit in couples[1] and lots were drawn for who should sit next to Astrid, daughter of the nobleman Vigfus, Eyjolf always drew the lot to sit beside her; but no one saw them talk together more than other people. Still, many people said that it would turn out that he would get a wife there. The feast came to an end, and it had been held magnificently and people were sent away with gifts. Eyjolf went on viking raids for four summers, and was thought an excellent fellow and a brave man; he acquired a good reputation and a lot of money.

One winter a man called Thorstein came to Voss, a relative of the brothers who had a farm in Oppland. He told them his problem, which was that a berserk[2] called Asgaut had challenged him to a duel[3] because

---

1. M.'s *tólfmenningr* (literally "drinking in groups of twelve") appears nowhere else. What is obviously meant is *tvímenningr* — "drinking in pairs from a single horn". When this was done, a man and a woman commonly shared each horn so far as the numbers of each sex present allowed — see Snorri's *Ynglinga saga* ch. 37, and *Egils saga* chs. 7, 48. It was probably regarded as morally lax, with strong sexual overtones, hence the stress on the discretion of Eyjolf and Astrid.

2. Berserks ("bear-shirts") were subject in battle to fits in which they foamed at the mouth, chewed the rims of their shields, howled like beasts, and were endowed with preternatural strength and immunity to wounds as long as the fit lasted. *Vatnsdæla saga* even states (ch. 9) that some beserks wore animal skins instead of coats of mail, but this may be an over-literal view of a figurative expression. But the term was also applied, as here, to gangsters who went round Norway challenging men to duels as a means of extorting money, property or their female relatives from them, (cf. *Grettis saga* ch. 19, *Egils saga*

he had refused him his sister, and he asked them to give him support in the duel so that the viking wouldn't infringe his rights. He said, however, that Asgaut had laid low many of his men; he said he would lose his sister if they wouldn't support him — "I'm not strong enough for a duel unless I get the benefit of your good luck[4] as well." They didn't like to refuse his request to go.

Now they went with him to Oppland, taking thirty men with them, and came to the place where the encounter was to be. Then they asked round among their men who would like to win himself a wife by going onto the island against Asgaut. But although the woman was thought desirable, nobody was prepared to do that to get her.

Then the brothers asked Eyjolf to hold Thorstein's shield for him. Eyjolf answered that he hadn't done that for anyone, not even for himself — "and I shall not be best pleased to have his death on my hands — I can't see any credit in that. But if this chap gets killed on us, do we then leave it at that and go home, or do we get a second man and a third, and add to our disgrace the more men we lose? And there won't be much honour in our journey if we go back without avenging him, if he's been killed before our very eyes. Ask me rather to go onto the

ch. 64). In either sense, berserks are rarely Icelanders (*Njáls saga* ch. 103 is an exception, with an obviously Christian propagandist motive) and they are always regarded with revulsion. Some Icelanders are given the nickname "berserk" (see ch. 22 below), but not shown in the berserk fury, and here the word may have meant merely "a man of exceptional size and strength", as sometimes in modern Icelandic.

3. Duels were originally held on islands to ensure that only the proper and equal number of supporters were present with each man, and that the loser could not get away without due payment. The practice probably arose to settle disputes with limited bloodshed, but became a social menace because aggressive challenges could be used by strong men as a way of depriving others of what belonged to them.

4. *gæfa* — "influence" or "good luck". This quality or its absence was believed to be part of a man's character — see. P. Hallberg, "The concept of *gipta* – *gæfa* – *hamingja* in Old Norse Literature", in *Proceedings of the First International Saga Conference*, London 1973, pp. 143–83.

island against the berserk myself; that would be helping my friends, but I won't do what you have asked."

They thanked him profusely, but it seemed to them that it would be putting a lot at stake to risk him. He said: "It seems to me that none of us has the right to go back home if he isn't avenged, and I should think it worse to fight against the berserk if your kinsman had already been killed."

Then they went forward, and Ivar offered to hold his shield for him. Eyjolf replied: "That's well offered, but I shall be the person most concerned about it, and it's quite true, that old proverb that 'self's hand is safest'." Then they went onto the island. The berserk said: "Is that great brute going to fight me?"

Eyjolf said: "You're afraid to fight me, aren't you? Perhaps you haven't behaved so well, when you're afraid of a big man but vaunt yourself over a little one."

"That doesn't apply to me," said he, "but I'll explain to you the rules of the duel. Six marks[5] shall ransom me off the island if I'm wounded."

Eyjolf replied: "I don't feel obliged to keep any rules towards you when you decide for yourself how much you're worth, because in my country the price you put on yourself would be thought fit payment for a slave."

Eyjolf was to strike first,[6] and with his first blow the sword hit the tail of the shield, and off went the tail and the berserk's foot with it.

---

5. Recent editors have "three", but ultra-violet light shows that M.'s reading is probably ví —"six"; but this remains a very small value for a free man, whose usual price seems to have been either one *hundrað silfrs* (120 ounces of silver), which was worth 15 marks in silver, or twice that amount (further see Luðvík Ingvarsson — *Refsingar á Íslandi á þjóðveldistímanum*, Reykjavík, 1970, pp. 349–59, and ch. 14 note 3 below). All the same, Eyjolf is exaggerating — *Egils saga* ch. 80 makes the average "value" of a slave in Iceland one and a half marks.

6. Duellists struck alternate blows, the man who had been challenged striking first — see *Kormáks saga* ch. 10.

From this exploit Eyjolf gained much fame, and then went home with the brothers. Now he was offered a great deal of money, but said he hadn't done it for the money nor for the woman, but rather because of his friendship with the brothers. Asgaut ransomed himself off the island and lived on as a cripple.

After that Eyjolf asked for the hand of Astrid, Vigfus's daughter. Ivar and Hreidar were there to put his case, saying that he was a man of noble descent and had a high position in Iceland and powerful support from his relatives; and they declared it likely that his future would be great. Then Eyjolf said: "Perhaps Astrid's kinsmen may think my suit shows great pride, but many in Iceland know that we have a noble lineage and much property."

Vigfus said: "This shall be her destiny, though something no less outstanding was intended for our kinswoman." She was married to him and went out to Iceland with him.

CHAPTER 5

THERE WAS A man called Bödvar — he was the son of Kari the Viking and brother to Sigurd, Vigfus's father. Bödvar was the father of Astrid, the mother of Eirik, the father of Astrid, the mother of Olaf Tryggvason.[1] Kari the Viking was the son of Eymund the Field-Spoiler, son of Thorir. Bödvar was also the father of Olof, mother of Gizur the White.[2] When Eyjolf and Astrid reached

---

1. King of Norway 995–1000; this genealogy is unreliable in a number of details, and its three earliest generations are little more than legend; more is said of them in *Áns saga bogsveigis*.

2. A major figure on the Christian side during the crisis which led to Iceland's conversion to Christianity in the year 1000; his son Ísleif became the first native bishop. See also *Njáls saga* chs. 46 ff., *Íslendingabók* chs. 7, 9.

Iceland, Ingjald was dead; then Eyjolf took over the farm and the chieftaincy. Ingjald had a daughter called Ulfeid, who was married to Narfi of Hrisey. The children of Eyjolf and Astrid were four in number. Their eldest son was called Thorstein, and he was given his share of the inheritance when he got married; he lived the rest of his life at Holar in Eyjafjord, and he doesn't come into the story much. The second was called Vigfus — he married Hallfrid, the daughter of Thorkel the Tall from Myvatn. The youngest son was called Glum, and the daughter Helga — she was married to Steingrim of Sigluvik, and their son was Thorvald Chatterbox,[3] who comes into the plot later on. But Vigfus died not long after getting married, leaving one child which lived for only a short time afterwards, and for that reason a half share of the whole property with Glum and Astrid came to Hallfrid — Eyjolf being dead by this time. Then Thorkel the Tall moved to Thvera with his son Sigmund, who was a man of ability and planned to make himself into a chief if he could get an advantageous marriage and the support of the relatives who would come with it.

There was a man called Thorir who lived at Espihol; he was the son of Hamund Corpse-Skin and Ingunn, daughter of Helgi the Lean. He was married to Thordis Kadalsdottir, and their children were Thorarin; Thorvald Hook, who lived at Grund in Eyjafjord; Thorgrim, who lived at Mödrufell; Ingunn, who married Thord the priest of Frey; and Vigdis, who married Sigmund.

Later, Thorkel and Sigmund began to make things difficult for Astrid on the farm, and the land was divided in half, the part without

---

3. Thorvald *tasaldi* is unknown outside the texts translated here, and his nickname is difficult. The interpretation given here connects with Modern Norwegian *tas* — "babble", "chatter"; or it may be related to New Norwegian *tase*, modern Icelandic *tása* — "to tug, pull", and mean something like "overbearing man" — cf. also modern Icelandic *tasvigur* — "energetic".

a house on it falling to Glum and Astrid — and they set up a farm at Borgarhol. But Glum didn't bother himself with the farmwork, and was thought rather backward in his development. He was always reserved and spoke little, a tall man with rather slanting eyebrows,[4] straight fair hair, slim and thought to be rather slow-witted; he didn't go to social gatherings. Now the property belonging to him and Astrid was being eaten into, and the upkeep of their household became difficult. But Sigmund and Thorkel pushed them about, and they got the smaller part of everything.

There was a temple to Frey south of the river at Hripkelsstadir.[5] Thorarin of Espihol was a clever and popular man but his brother Thorvald Hook was a duellist and quarrelsome. Sigmund Thorkelsson thought himself an important man when he got himself related to the people at Espihol. Glum told his mother that he wanted to go abroad — "I can see that I'm not going to get anywhere here, but perhaps I may get some good luck from my noble relatives. I'm not prepared to put up with Sigmund's oppression, but I can see that I'm not able to stand up to him yet. But don't let go of the land, even if your position gets difficult." Glum was fifteen years old when he decided to go abroad.

---

4. *skollbrúnn* cf. Modern Icelandic *skolli* — "sly person", "fox" — (ie. perhaps originally "one who is crooked"); the other possible interpretation is "with eyebrows close together or joined".

5. ie. South of the Thvera ("Cross River") — see map. It floods violently each spring and is liable to changes of course, so its exact line cannot be reconstructed, nor can the shrine be exactly placed, or the field "the Sure Giver" with which it is associated (see ch. 7). The historical existence in Iceland of buildings set aside for heathen worship is now in doubt (see Olaf Olsen, *Hørg, Hov og Kirke*, Copenhagen 1966, pp. 167–209, English summary on pp. 283–5), and their presence in the sagas may reflect only the assumptions natural to 13th century Christian authors. But if there ever was a temple, it was most likely on the low ground by the river Thvera (cf. Glum's dream in ch. 26), and flood erosion will have destroyed all traces of it.

CHAPTER 6

Glum's trip abroad

NOW WE COME to Glum's trip abroad. As soon as he landed, he went up to Voss to see Vigfus. When he got to the farm he saw a great crowd of people there, with sports and amusements of all kinds, and it seemed clear to him that everything there was done in the grand manner. But since he saw many notable men, he didn't know which one was Vigfus, his kinsman. But he worked out who it was when he saw a big and noble-looking man in the high seat, wearing a black[1] cloak with a hood and playing with a gold-inlaid spear. Then he went up to him and greeted him.

Vigfus returned his greeting graciously, asking what sort of man he was; and he said he was an Icelander from Eyjafjord. Then Vigfus asked about his kinsman Eyjolf and his daughter Astrid, and Glum replied that he was dead — "but Astrid is still alive." Vigfus asked what children of theirs were living, and Glum told him about his brothers and sister.

---

1. *Blár*, usually "blue", but cf. the expressions *blár sem Hel* — "as black as Hell", *kolblár* — "coal-black", *blámenn* — "black men". The putting on of black clothes in sagas is generally followed by the wearer killing someone — cf. *Völsunga saga* ch. 11 and *Hrafnkels saga* ch. 3; but there are one or two exceptions (eg. *Bjarnar saga Hitdælakappa* ch. 11, *Fóstbræðra saga* ch. 23), and Marina Mundt has suggested (*Proceedings of the First International Saga Conference* pp. 357–8) that the symbol's meaning may be gathered from *Þiðreks saga* ch. 174 (ed. C.R. Unger, Kristiania 1853) — *Oc merkir blár litr kallt brióst oc grimt hiarta* — "And black/blue colour indicates a cold heart and a grim nature." This would fit all the contexts well, and although *Víga-Glums saga* and *Bjarnar saga* are probably too early to be influenced by *Þiðreks saga*, this sense may already have been traditional in Scandinavia when it appeared there.

Then he told him that it was one of their sons who stood before him. But when he had said that, the conversation went no further.[2] Glum asked to be shown to a seat, but Vigfus said he didn't know how much of what he had said was true, and allocated to him a seat at the outer end of the lower bench and paid him little respect. Glum was taciturn and unsociable — while other people were drinking or having some other amusement, he lay down with his cloak over his head. He was thought an idiot there.

A feast was held at the beginning of Winter, and sacrifice made to the spirits,[3] and everyone had to take part in this observance. Glum stayed in his place and didn't join in. As the evening wore on and everyone had arrived, there was not so much enjoyment as one would have expected from the welcome they had had and the meeting of so many friends as had come together there. And on the day that people had arrived at the feast Glum had not gone out to meet them or invited anyone to sit beside him or in his place. When they were seated at table it was announced that a man called Björn, nicknamed Iron Skull, had come to the farm with eleven other men. He was a great berserk, and was in the habit of coming to feasts where there were a lot of people, and bandying words with men to see if anyone would say something he could object to — and then he used to challenge them to duels. But Vigfus asked them to be careful what they said — "and that's less of a

---

2. M. *þá reitisk ekki af um talit*; *reitask á*, used impersonally, means "to come to something", and a similar construction using *reitask af* ought then to mean "to fall off, cease". But this is found nowhere else, and does not fit the context very well; on balance, it seems best to amend *af* to *á*.

3. The *dísir*, female guardian spirits, probably originally those of dead ancestors — cf. the heathen English (midwinter) feast of *Mōdraniht* — "Night of the mothers", described by Bede (*De Temporum Ratione* ch. 15, in *Bedae Venerabilis Opera* I, *Patrologia Latina* vol. 90, ed. J.P. Migne, Paris 1862, col. 356); but the word *dísir* was used in somewhat varying senses — see Turville-Petre ed. p. 60 and his *Myth and Religion of the North*, London 1964, pp. 221–7. The beginning of winter was about the middle of October.

humiliation than getting more serious trouble from him" — and they promised him they would do that.

Björn came striding into the hall and looked[4] round for greetings from people, and asked the outermost man at the higher bench whether he was as tough as he was — but he said "far from it." Then he asked them one after another, until he came in front of the high seat. They resorted to various forms of words, but it came down to the fact that nobody said he was as tough as Björn. And when he came in front of Vigfus he asked where Vigfus knew of any champion who might be set alongside him, and he said he didn't know his equal. Then Björn said: "Well answered! — And sensibly, as was to be expected. You're a very honourable man, and your life has gone along with your wishes for a long time; no disgrace has come your way, only honour. So it's just as well that I don't have to say anything to you but good. But all the same, I want to ask you if you think yourself equal to me."

He replied: "When I was young and went on viking raids, and achieved some small degree of fame, well, I don't know but what I might have been a match for you then; but it's far too late for that now that I'm old and feeble."

Björn turned away and proceeded outwards along the other bench, still asking if they thought they were as tough as he was; but they replied that they were not as tough as he was. Then he came to where Glum was lying along the bench.

"Why is that man lying like that and not sitting up?" said Björn.

Glum's neighbours at table answered and spoke up on his behalf, saying that he was so moronic that no attention could be paid to what he said. Björn kicked at him and told him to sit up like other people — and asked him if he was as tough as himself. Glum said there was no need for

---

4. The participants in a feast sat at table on benches ranged along the walls, with the chief either at the inner end or in the middle of the "senior" side (ie. the one to the right as one came in), and the least honoured men nearest the door at the outer end.

him to interfere with him, and that he didn't know about his toughness — "But I certainly don't want to equate myself with you, because out in Iceland a man who carried on in the way you behave would be called a fool. But here everyone minds his tongue better than anywhere I've ever come across." After that he leaps up and at him, snatches off his helmet, then grabs a firebrand and strikes him a blow between the shoulders which made the "hero" stumble, and immediately another, and one after the other, so that he fell. And when he tried to get to his feet Glum hit him on the head, and went on doing so until he got outside the door.

But when Glum made to go back to his seat, Vigfus had come into the middle of the hall with all of them, and then he welcomed his kinsman warmly, saying that he had now given proof that he was of his family — "now I shall honour you as befits us both." He said that the reason for his first reaction was that he hadn't seemed very promising to him — "I wanted to wait until you earned your place in the family by some piece of bravery" — and now he led him to a seat beside him. Glum said he would have accepted that place even if it had been offered sooner.

The next day the death of Björn was reported. Vigfus offered Glum the succession to his power and position, and Glum said he would like to accept, but wanted first to go out to Iceland, so that his inheritance wouldn't be acquired by those whom he didn't want to possess it. He said he would come back as soon as possible. Vigfus said he thought it was Glum's destiny to enhance his own and his family's honour in Iceland.

In the summer Vigfus had a ship made ready for Glum and gave him the cargo on it and a lot of money in gold and silver, and said: "I have a feeling that we shan't see each other again, but I'll give you some special treasures, a cloak and spear and sword on which our family has placed great reliance; and while you keep these precious things, I expect that you won't lose your position — but I have my fears about what may happen if you let them go." After that they parted.

CHAPTER 7

Glum's return to Iceland

N OW GLUM WENT out to Iceland and home to Thvera. He met his mother immediately, and she greeted him warmly and told him about the unjust behaviour of Thorkel and Sigmund — but told him to endure it with patience, saying that she was not capable of opposing them. After that he rode home to the farm boundary. Then he saw that the boundary fence had been moved over onto his side, and then he recited a verse:

1. Nearer it goes to me and mine
    Necklace-leafed lady, to our kin's grief.
    Thin goes our joy, and green
    The fence runs, nearer than we had sensed.
    Sadly the land is shamed
    I say, debased from mine,
    Yet still in the stir of steel
    I'll not stay bereft of what my father left me.[1]

But meanwhile, events out here in Iceland had gone like this: Sigmund was pestering Astrid and wanted to get her off the farm. In the autumn while Glum had been abroad, two of Thorkel and Sigmund's cows had gone missing, and they thought they had been stolen and suspected some

---

1. On the problems involved in translating the verses in sagas, see Introduction pp. 22-7. "green/the fence" (lines 3–4); the home meadow of Icelandic farmsteads was often surrounded by a wall of green turves.

slaves belonging to Astrid, and said that they had eaten them dried,[2] and in the spring summoned them on a charge of theft. But these slaves were much the most reliable Astrid had, for their overseeing and labour. She thought she would hardly be able to work the farm if they were taken away, and went to see her son Thorstein and told him how aggressive Thorkel and Sigmund were being, and asked him to defend the slaves.

"I would rather pay compensation for them than let them be outlawed on a false charge, if there's no better choice; and it seems to me that you ought to stand up for me now and show by what you say that you come of a good family."

Thorstein said that he thought the case would be put forward by the other side with the intention of pursuing it with all the power of their relatives. "It seems advisable to me, if these men are essential to you, that I should make a contribution to the compensation and try to get it accepted."

She said: "I have a feeling that the only compensation they'll accept will be something intended to damage us; but since little support can be looked for from you, the matter will have to be put in their hands."

Now the greatest asset of the land at Thvera was a field which was called "the Sure Giver",[3] because it was never barren; and it had been

---

2. M. *einætum* — Turville-Petre suggests the meaning "alone, secretly", Ranisch "raw", but modern Eyjafjord dialect uses the word to describe dried fish — a traditional Icelandic food (*Íslenzk fornrit* IX pp. 20–1). In the Faroe Islands meat is still prepared in the same way, and such an unobtrusive method of preparation, involving no fire, would obviously have an appeal for thieves, which may explain why Thorkel and Sigmund feel it unnecessary to produce more circumstantial evidence.

3. M. *Vitazgjafi*, "the Sure Giver", seems contextually superior to the older version's *Fitjaskafi*, "meadow scraper", and is parallelled in a document of 1397 (*Diplomatarium Islandicum* IV, 234), and in three contexts in Norway, at least one of which is connected with fertility — see Turville-Petre pp. 61–2 and Anne Holtsmark in *Maal og Minne* 1933, pp. 111–33. The field is presumably to be associated with the nearby temple of Frey, the god of fertility.

shared out when the land was divided, so that the two sides had it in alternate years. Now Astrid said to Sigmund and his father: "It seems to me that you want very much to prevent me from prospering, and you can see that there is no manager here; but rather than let the slaves be handed over I'll put the case into your judgement." They said that was the wiser course. They now consulted, and their decision was that they would either award themselves the damages to be paid on the slaves' behalf, or else they would outlaw them. And Thorstein made such a poor showing in the case that they won the right to award their own damages, and made over to themselves sole possession of the field, intending in this way to get hold of the entire property by plucking away the support which had previously done most to maintain Astrid. And in the summer which was then approaching she was supposed to have the field if justice had been done.

But in the summer, when people had gone to the Assembly where this case was settled, a herdsman going round the pastures found the cows in a hollow which had been covered over by drifting snow early the previous winter, and now the slander against the slaves was clear. And when father and son heard that the cows had been found, they offered to pay for the field but refused to give up possession of it. But Astrid said that the amends made for the slander wouldn't be excessive even if she got what belonged to her — "And I'll either have what is mine or do without. Although nobody is willing to set things to rights, I'll just wait, and I expect Glum will come out to Iceland and set my case straight."

Sigmund replied: "You'll wait long enough for help from that quarter, when the likelier of your sons stands by and does nothing."

She said: "Pride and injustice often come to a bad end, Sigmund, and perhaps that may apply to you."

A little later in the summer Glum came out to Iceland, and after staying briefly with his ship, went to his farm with a lot of wealth. But he had the same nature as before, reacting little and behaving as if he hadn't heard what had happened out here in the meantime. Every morning he slept until breakfast time,[4] and he didn't bother about the farm. That summer he and his mother should have had the field if justice had been done.

Sigmund's herds caused them a great deal of damage and were in their meadow every morning. One morning Astrid woke Glum and said that Sigmund's cattle had got into the paddock and were trying to break down the hayricks — "and I haven't the strength to drive them away, but the farmhands are out at work."

He replied: "You haven't ordered me to work very much, and I won't take offence at this." He jumped up, took his horse and a wooden stick in his hand, beat the cattle vigorously and went on belabouring them until they came into Thorkel and Sigmund's paddock — and there he let them do what damage they liked. Thorkel stayed at home looking after the hayricks during the mornings, and Sigmund went out with the farmhands.

Thorkel said to Glum: "You can expect that people won't let you get away with it if you injure their livestock, even if you think you've done well for yourself abroad."

Glum said that all his cattle were unhurt so far, "but if they come causing damage to our property again, they won't all come off unscathed, and you might as well feel pleased about that, because you won't get it changed; and we won't put up with damage from your animals any longer."

Then Thorkel said: "You're playing the big man now Glum, but to us you seem the same sort of idiot now as when you went abroad. And we're not going to make our plans to fit your big mouth." Glum turned homewards, and was seized with laughter, and it gripped him so that his

---

4. *dagmál* — about 9 a.m., when a major meal was eaten; it was usual to work from *rismál* — "getting up time", about 6 a.m., until time for the meal.

face became pale and tears the size of hailstones started from his eyes. And he was often affected in this way afterwards, when the mood to kill was on him.

CHAPTER 8

The slaying of Sigmund

IT'S SAID THAT when autumn was well advanced, Astrid came one morning to talk to Glum again, woke him up and told him to get ready for work; she said the haymaking would be finished today if things were done properly. Sigmund and his men had finished their haymaking some time ago — "and early this morning Sigmund and Vigdis went to the Sure Giver field, and they must be feeling pleased with themselves, seeing they have the field that we ought to have by rights."

Then Glum got up, but still wasn't ready before breakfast time. Then he took the black cloak, and the gold-inlaid spear in his hand, and had his horse saddled. Astrid said: "You're dressing up a bit much for going haymaking, my son." He replied: "I don't often go to work, but when I do I'll both get a lot done and be well equipped for it. However, I can't very well set to with the labouring; I'm going to ride over to Holar and take up an invitation from my brother Thorstein."

After that he rode south over the river. But when he came to the field he took out the pin fastening his cloak; and there they were in the field, Vigdis and Sigmund. And when Vigdis saw him, she went to meet him and greeted him — "It seems a pity to us that our relationship with you is so cool, and we would like it to be better, by all means."

Glum replied: "Nothing has happened yet to stop our relationship from being good — but the reason I came over here is that the pin has come out of my cloak, and I'd like you to sew it on in a knot." [1]

She said she'd be pleased to do that, and she did. Glum looked across the field and said: "The Sure Giver hasn't failed yet." Then he put on the cloak and took the spear in his hand. After that he turned on Sigmund brandishing the spear, and as he sprang up to meet him Glum immediately struck him on the head, and Sigmund needed no more. Then Glum went to Vigdis and told her to go home — "and tell Thorkel that Sigmund isn't able to get back from the field by himself." Glum rode up to Holar and told his brother nothing about it. But when Thorstein saw his equipment, that he'd brought both cloak and spear, and then found blood on the spear's ornamentation, he asked if he had used it recently. He replied:

"That's right, it didn't occur to me to mention," said Glum, "that I killed Sigmund Thorkelsson today."

Thorstein said: "Thorkel and his relatives at Espihol will regard that as news."

Glum said: "It's an old saying that blood will have blood at once,[2] but they'll think little of it after a bit." Glum stayed there with his brother for three nights, and then he made ready to go home. Thorstein offered to go with him, but Glum said it wasn't necessary: "You look after your farm. I'll ride straight home to Thvera — they won't be so anxious to follow up this business." Glum went back home to Thvera.

But when this piece of news became known, Thorkel went to see Thorarin and asked for advice and support from him. He said:

"Now perhaps Astrid may say that he hasn't grown up on his legs for nothing."

Thorkel replied: "I think he's grown up on legs he won't be able to walk on."

---

1. *Nisting*, here translated "knot", could be the same as *nist* or *nisti*, a brooch or pin, but that would hardly fit here, and cf. Old High German *nestilo*, Old English *nostle* — "a band"; cf. also *Laxdæla saga*, ch. 75.
2. *Blóðnætr eru bráðastar*, literally "blood nights are most hasty".

Thorarin said: "That's as may be; you've treated them unjustly for a long time and tried to drive them out of their property,[3] and you haven't considered what was to be expected of the descendents of a man like Eyjolf, who was both of great family and the bravest of men. But we have a very great obligation to Glum because of being related, and with you through marriage, and the case seems to me to be an awkward one if Glum follows it up as I expect he will."

Then Thorkel went home, and the matter rested over the winter. Glum had somewhat more men during the winter than usual.

CHAPTER 9

About Glum's dreams

IT'S SAID THAT Glum had a dream one night. He seemed to be standing outside on his farm and looking out towards the fjord. He dreamed he saw a woman walking in through the district, and she turned directly towards Thvera; but she was so big that her shoulders touched the mountains on both sides. And he dreamed that he went out of the farmyard to meet her and invited her to stay with him — and then he woke up. It seemed remarkable to everyone, but he said this:

"It's a great and notable dream, and I explain it like this: Vigfus my grandfather must now be dead, and the woman who was taller than the mountains as she walked must have been his personal spirit.[1] He was,

---

3. *færa þau við útgarða* might more generally be rendered "to drive them to the wall"; the *útgarðar* were the dikes marking the boundary between meadows and wild pasture. But the specific sense seems more appropriate, both here and in *Gísla saga* II, ch. 5.

1. *hamingja* — "personal spirit", related to *hamr* — "skin", "shape", here used synonymously with *fylgja* — "protective accompanying spirit"; it was believed that after a man's death his *fylgja* attached itself to another member of the same family. Further, see Turville-Petre, *Myth and Religion of the North*, pp. 227–30.

after all, honoured above other men in most things, and his personal spirit will seek out a home for herself with me."

And in the summer, when ships arrived from Norway, the death of Vigfus was announced. Then Glum recited a verse:

2. I saw her walk with her island
    (her wrist the hawk's small island)
    Like Earth, in the fjord of islands,
    Wrist-spanned with icy silver, that guardian spirit.
    So the goddess who ends the battle
    Seemed in my awesome dream,
    (She who fells you, troubler of armies)
    Helmeted between the fells to stand.[2]

In the spring Thorkel went to see Thorvald Hook and Thorir's other sons and asked for their support in this case. And he talked about his obligation to his daughter[3] and the many friendly things he and his son Sigmund had done for them. Thorvald went to see Thorarin and said it would be disgraceful if they didn't follow up their kinsman's case; he added that he wanted to give all the help that was in his power — "and it's now obvious that Glum intends to increase his own influence by the killing of Sigmund, and we don't want to be worse respected in the district."

Thorarin said: "It seems to me that it may be difficult to support the case in any way that we'll be likely to benefit from. And what's more, as Glum grows up it's not unlikely that he'll show the nature of his relatives and ancestors. I go into it more reluctantly than you, because

---

2. For a full analysis of this stanza, see Introduction, pp. 25–7

3. Thorkel refers to his daughter-in-law Vigdis as "daughter". The older version's text is damaged, but appears to have meant something like: "And he (Thorvald) talked about his obligation to his sister (Vigdis) and the many friendly deeds he (Thorkel) had done for them."

the credit to be got from quarrelling with Glum seems uncertain to me. But I won't be pleased if our disgrace increases either."

But with persuasion, Thorarin Thorisson prepared a case against Glum at the General Assembly for the killing of Sigmund. Glum prepared a case against Thorkel the Tall for slander against the slaves and another against Sigmund, and summoned him for theft, saying that he had killed him on his own property. He summoned him as outside the protection of the law, since he had fallen on Glum's property, and dug up Sigmund's body. After that the cases went to the General Assembly in this state, and Glum then sought out his relatives Gizur the White and Teit, son of Ketilbjörn from Mosfell, and Asgrim son of Ellida-Grim to ask for support, and told them the whole state of affairs and the aggression and unjust behaviour of father and son and the many slights he had suffered. He said he was relying on support from them for justice according to the law, but that he himself would be in charge of his case. They all said they had a duty to see that his affairs were not controlled by his enemies, and said they would be delighted if the family were to be strengthened by his advancement.

Time passed at the Assembly until the court went into session, and the men of Espihol raised the case about the slaying, more[4] with the encouragement of those who had old grievances to remember than with any certainty that it would be legally watertight. Glum produced his case against Thorkel, and the conflicting pleas came before the court; Glum had a great deal of support from relatives and friends. And when called on for his defence, Glum said: "It's like this, as must be well known to a lot of people, that you've prepared the case with more folly than legal accuracy, because I killed Sigmund on my own property; and before I rode to the Assembly I summoned him as outside the protection of the law." He named his witnesses to that and so refuted the charge, and those relatives supported him, so that Sigmund was held to have

---

4. *meir* — "more" has apparently been omitted by the scribe of M.

fallen outside the law. After that, Glum brought forward the case against Thorkel for attempting to defraud him[5] of his property, and it turned out badly for Thorkel, because the witnesses agreed with Glum and no legal defence could be found — and it got to the point that Thorkel was going to be outlawed. A settlement was sought with Glum. He said there were two choices open: either he would pursue the case, or else Thorkel was to sell him the land at Thvera for the price Glum was prepared to set on it, and that was no more than half its value. "And Thorkel can expect, if he is outlawed, that we shan't both come to the Assembly next summer."

And now Thorkel's friends prevailed on him to settle out of court, and he took the best course open to him — settled the case and sold Glum the land, but was to live there for the following six months, and they were then to call it settled, and the men of Espihol were annoyed at this ending to the case. And from this time on, relations between Glum and the people at Espihol were never healed.

Before Thorkel went away from Thvera, he went to the shrine of Frey, taking an old ox there with him, and spoke in this way:

"Oh Frey," he said, "who hast long been my trust, and hast received many oblations from me and repaid them well, now I give thee this ox, to the end that Glum may depart from the land at Thvera under a compulsion no less than that by which I go now. And let there now appear some token of whether thou hast accepted my prayer or not."

And the ox started violently, bellowed and fell down dead, and it seemed to Thorkel[6] that that was a good sign, and he was calmer in his

---

5. M. *bekráð*, probably a mistake for *brekráð*, (though one MS of *Ljósvetninga saga* also has the form without the first r — *Íslenzk fornrit* X p. 24, fn. 2); made up of *brek* — "fraud" and *ráð* — "a plan, intention". The term is unknown in *Grágás*, but both halves of it occur in other compounds (eg. *breksekt* — "a fraudulent institution of outlawry proceedings", *fjörráð* — "intent to murder").

6. M. omits *þorkatli* — "to Thorkel".

mind, now that he thought that his prayer had been accepted. Then he went north to Myvatn[7] and lived there, and his part in the story is finished.

CHAPTER 10

GLUM NOW BEGAN to have great prestige in the district. There was a man living at Lon in Hörgardal called Gunnstein, an impressive man and rich, generally accepted as one of the important people. He had a wife called Hlif. Their son was called Thorgrim, and he was known by his mother's name and called Hlifarson because she lived longer than Gunnstein; she was a woman of great distinction. Thorgrim was full of manly qualities and became an outstanding man. Their second son was called Grim, who was known as Bankleg. Their daughter was called Halldora — she was a beautiful woman and good-natured. She was thought to be among the best matches of all because of her relatives and above all for her intelligence and practical ability. This was the woman whose hand Glum asked for; he said he would not need to say much about his family, nor about his property or style of life — "that must be well known to you; but I have decided on this match for myself, provided it fits in with her relatives' wishes." This request was given a favourable answer — she was betrothed to Glum, and a great deal of money went with her; and their wedding was held fittingly. And now his position was even more respected than before.

There was a man called Thorvald Refsson,[1] who lived at Bard in

---

7. In fact, Myvatn is due east of Eyjafjord, about 50 km. from Thvera, but people in Eyjafjord have always referred to the two counties in the North-East corner of Iceland as "up North" —- see Stefán Einarsson in *Journal of English and Germanic Philology* 43 (1944), pp. 265–85.
1. M. "Rein's son", but Ref of Bard is mentioned in *Landnámabók*.

Fljot. He was married to Thurid, daughter of Thord from Höfdi. Their children were Klaufi and Thorgerd, who became the wife of Thorarin of Espihol. Thorvald Hook of Grund married Thorkatla from Thjorsardal. Hlenni the Old, son of Örnolf Bagback, lived at Vidines and married Oddkatla, daughter of Oddkel from Thjorsardal.[2] There was a man called Gizur who was the son of Kadal — he lived at Tjarnir in the Eyjafjord valley; he had a wife called Saldis — she was a fine housewife. Gizur was also among the more important farmers, and very wealthy. Two daughters of him and Saldis are known, called Thordis and Herthrud, beautiful women and very elegant; they were thought good matches and grew up at home there. Gizur's brother was called Runolf — he was the father of Valgerd, mother of Eyjolf of Mödruvellir. The daughter of Kadal was Thordis, who married Thorir of Espihol, and their children were as has been said earlier. Thorgrim Thorisson was not the son of Thordis, but he was legitimate nonetheless.[3] Thorgrim was a distinguished and capable man. He rode to visit Gizur on the errand of asking for his daughter Thordis as wife. Those who put forward this request were his brothers, and some friends who were relatives of the woman and thought they had some right to a say in arranging the marriage of their kinswoman; and they considered the proposal made to them an excellent one. But Thorgrim was refused the woman, although it seemed to everyone that he had proposed a marriage between equals — and his brothers and kinsmen were offended.

---

2. Thorkatla, Oddkatla and Una were probably sisters (see chs. 17, 18); they came from Thjorsardal, central South Iceland. In other sources, Hlenni's father is called Orm rather than Örnolf (*Landnámabók, Ljósvetninga saga* chs. 10ff., *Njáls saga* ch. 105).

3. This sentence may be to ease Christian sensibilities, for if Thorgrim had been the son of Thordis Kadalsdottir, he and Thordis, whom he asks to marry, would have been first cousins, between whom the church forbade marriage. The emphasis on Thorgrim's legitimacy is puzzling, since illegitimacy has never carried much social stigma in Iceland. The version of *Landnámabók* by Sturla Thordarson (†1284) agrees that he was not the son of Thordis but says nothing of his legitimacy; that by Hauk Erlendsson (†1334) merely lists him among the children of Thorir and Thordis.

CHAPTER 11

A MAN COMES into the story who was called Arnor and nicknamed Red Cheek. He was the son of Steinolf, son of Ingjald,
and Glum's first cousin. He had been a sea-going merchant for a long
time, and was well thought of and always stayed with Glum when he
was out here in Iceland. He raised the suggestion that Glum should ask
for a wife for him. Glum inquired what woman he wanted to ask for.
Arnor said: "Thordis the daughter of Gizur, who was refused to
Thorgrim Thorisson."

Glum replied: "I don't think there's much prospect in that, because so
far as I can see there's no difference between you and Thorgrim except
that he has a good farm, a lot of money and powerful support from his
relatives, whereas you have no farm and not enough property. And I
don't want to do Gizur the injustice of preventing him from arranging
what he wants for his daughter, because Gizur deserves well from me."

Arnor said: "I shall have the advantage of good relatives too if I can
make a better marriage as a result of you putting my case. Promise him
your friendship and then he'll give the woman, because this would have
been called a fair match if a fine man like Thorgrim hadn't been turned
away already."

Glum let himself be persuaded and went with him to see Gizur, and
put the matter to him. Gizur replied: "People may say, Glum," he said,
"that I'm misguided if I give my daughter to your kinsman Arnor when
I saw fit not to give her to Thorgrim."

Glum answered: "That's a fair comment, but I must explain that if
you will agree to our request my friendship will come in return."

Gizur said: "That seems to me to be worth a lot, but I suspect that hostility from other people may cancel it out."

Glum replied: "Well, you must make your own decision — but what you do will make a great difference to my attitude towards you."

Then Gizur said: "You shan't go away empty handed this time" — and he stretched out his hand and Arnor became engaged to the woman. But Glum offered to hold the wedding at Thvera in the autumn, and now they parted on these terms.

Arnor had some malt out at Gasar[1] and was going to fetch it himself with one servant. But Thorgrim Thorisson went to the baths on the day they were expected back with the malt, and they were at the baths at Hrafnagil, he and his six serving men along with him. But when Arnor and his servant were coming back up the valley and were about to ride across the river, Thorgrim said: "Now isn't this a good opportunity to go and meet Arnor and his party? We won't go without the malt anyway, even if we must do without the woman."

Thorgrim and his men went towards them with drawn swords, and when Arnor and his servant saw the odds against them they[2] plunged their horses into the water and so across the river. But the pack horses remained west of the river. Then Thorgrim spoke: "We're not completely out of luck. We'll drink the ale, even if they arrange the woman's marriage."

Thorgrim rode to South Espihol.[3] Thorir was now blind, but Thorgrim's companions were jubilant and laughed a great deal, and Thorir asked what they thought so funny. They said they didn't know

---

1. *Gásar* was in the middle ages a major trading centre, and the ruins of some booths can be seen there. There was a little exploratory excavation there at the turn of the century (see *Árbók hins íslenzka fornleifafélags* 1901, p. 18 and 1908 pp. 3–8), but none has been done since.
2. M. has "he", but the servant will hardly have stayed behind.
3. Modern Litlihóll; the farm now called Espihóll is the "North Espihol" of the saga. The original settlement by Hamund Corpse-Skin and his son Thorir was apparently at "South Espihol", but Thorir's eldest son Thorarin lived at North Espihol — see ch. 17.

which side would hold the feast first. They described their catch and the chase they had had — "and the bridegroom in the water!"

When Thorir heard that, he said: "Does it seem to you that you've done well for yourselves, that you're laughing so much, or what are you going to do now to get out of this? Do you think you can sleep here tonight and not need to do anything more? You don't know Glum's character if you think he'll approve of what's happened to his kinsman. I call it sensible to collect men; it's more than likely that Glum has gathered a large number already."

There was then a ford in the river where there is none now.[4] They gathered eighty fighting men during the night and put themselves in readiness on the front of the bluff at Espihol, because the ford in the river was right beside the slope.

But to return to Arnor — he went to Glum and told him about his expedition.

He said: "It hasn't come as any surprise to me that they wouldn't let things rest, and there's now some problem — disgrace if it is allowed to rest at that, but no very clear honour if the matter is pursued as it should be. But now we'll have to get our men together."

And when it was light the next morning, Glum came to the river with sixty men and tried to ride across. But the men of Espihol threw stones at them and the ride went no further; and Glum turned back, and they fought across the river with stones and other missiles; and many were wounded there, though none of them are named.

When the local people became aware of this, they rushed up in the course of the day and went in between the combatants, and peace was restored and it was asked what satisfaction the men of Espihol would

---

4. This ford, near North Espihol, is now nameless but passable to horses under favourable conditions; in ch. 22 M. calls it *Knarrarvað* — "ship ford" — but the river is not navigable and this should probably be *Kvamárvað*, since the small Kvarná river joins the main river near it.

offer for the insult they had inflicted on Arnor. But the reply was that no compensation would be paid merely because Arnor had run away from his packhorses. Then it was suggested that Glum should take part in asking for the hand of Herthrud,[5] daughter of Gizur, on behalf of Thorgrim, and that the match between Arnor and Thordis should not proceed unless Glum obtained this woman for Thorgrim. And it was thought that the girl who got Thorgrim would have the better match of the two. Now because many people exerted their influence in the matter, Glum promised his help; he went to see Gizur and raised the question and said:

"It may look like interference if I ask for wives both for my own kinsmen and for the people at Espihol, but so that the mishaps in the district may come to an end I shall think myself bound to pledge you my loyal friendship if you do what I want."

Gizur replied: "It seems best to me that you should have your way, because I think the offer made for my daughter is a good one." Both matches now went ahead. Arnor set up a farm at Uppsalir and Thorgrim lived at Mödrufell. Shortly afterwards Gizur died. Then Saldis[6] moved to Uppsalir. Arnor had a son with Thordis, called Steinolf. Thorgrim also had a son, and he was called Arngrim and was a promising lad all the time he was growing up.

---

5. M. here has *Amþríð*, a scribal error obviously caused by the proximity of the name Arnor.

6. M. has *Valdís* here and at the beginning of ch. 12, elsewhere *Saldís* (as in ch. 10); the error is probably due to the rarity of the name Saldis.

CHAPTER 12

About the kinsmen

SALDIS INVITED BOTH her grandsons home. Arngrim was two years older than Steinolf, and no boys grew up in Eyjafjord more popular or better endowed in every respect, and they were extremely fond of each other. When one was four years old and the other six they were playing one day, and Steinolf asked Arngrim to lend him a bronze toy horse.[1] Arngrim replied: "I'll give it you, because now it suits your age better than mine." And Steinolf told his grandma[2] what a good gift he had been given. She said it was nice that they were on such good terms.

There was a woman called Oddbjörg who went around that district, an entertaining character, wise and gifted with second sight. It was thought very important that housewives in the area should give her a good welcome, for what she said was rather influenced by the hospitality offered to her. She came to Uppsalir, and Saldis received her

---

1. Many bronze images of horses (and a few of oxen, bears and dogs) have been found in Norway, where they were used as royally authorised standard weights, and this toy is usually explained as one such — see A.W. Brøgger, *Ertog og øre*, Christiania 1921, pp. 87–92. But these weights are from the reign of Hakon V, and thus can hardly date from before his accession in 1286, long after the saga was written. Only one bronze toy horse has been found in Iceland, in a grave-mound at Thingvellir, S.W. Iceland; now lost, it is supposed to have dated from the late 10th century, and may have been an emblem replacing the real horse whose skeleton appears in a number of graves (see Gwyn Jones, *A History of the Vikings*, Oxford 1968, p. 331). It would give literary point to this episode to regard the horse as an ironic death symbol.

2. *fóstra*, literally "fostermother", but often used as an affectionate general term of relationship.

well and asked her to foretell something about the boys — "and make it something nice."

She said: "These are promising lads if their luck holds, but that seems doubtful to me."

Saldis said: "I suppose, in view of this piece of mockery, that you're not quite satisfied with your reception."

She replied: "This mustn't influence what you dish up — and you needn't be so sensitive."

Saldis said: "You ought to keep quiet if your forebodings aren't good."

She said: "I haven't said overmuch about it yet, but I don't think their fondness for each other will last very long."

Saldis said: "I should have thought good hospitality deserved something better, and you'll be driven away if you go round predicting evil."

Oddbjörg said: "I don't think I need restrain myself now that you are carrying on like this for no reason. What's more, I won't visit your home any more, and you can take that as you like. But I can tell you that they will be deadly enemies, and as a result things will get worse and worse in this district" — and Oddbjörg is out of the story.

CHAPTER 13

About Ingolf

IT HAPPENED ONE summer at the General Assembly that teams of men were competing at wrestling at Fangabrekka,[1] the Northerners against the men of the Westfirths, and the Northerners were getting the

---

1. *Fangabrekka* — "Wrestling Slope", a place set aside for the sport of *glíma*, Icelandic wrestling (which resembles Cumberland wrestling).

worst of it. Mar the son of Glum was captain of their team. A man called Ingolf came along, the son of Thorvald; his father lived in Rangarvellir.

Mar said: "You're a powerfully built man — you must be strong. Help me by joining the wrestling."

He replied: "I'll do it to please you."

Ingolf's opponent fell; another came along and a third, and so it went on. Now the Northerners took heart. Then Mar said: "If you need me to speak up for you, I'll come to your help; but what plans have you now?"

He said: "I haven't decided, but what I'd like best is to go north and take a job."

Mar said: "I want you to travel with me, and I'll get you a place."

Ingolf had some good stud mares and a stallion which he called Snowy Top. He went north from the General Assembly to Thvera and stayed there for a while. One day Mar asked what Ingolf intended to do with himself: "A foreman is needed here, and he'd have to be quite good with his hands. Here's a sledge for you to mend, and you're handy enough to be worth your keep if you can do it."

Ingolf said: "I would be very glad to get this job, but it has sometimes happened that people objected to having my horses in the pastures."

Mar replied: "No notice will be taken here of anything like that."

Now Ingolf worked on the sledge, and Glum came and looked at the workmanship. "This is well made," he said. "What are your plans?"

Ingolf replied: "I haven't decided."

Glum said: "I need a foreman. Are you used to that sort of job at all?"

He replied: "Not much in places like this, but I would like to stay with you."

Glum said: "Why not? I see that you and Mar get on well together."

Now Mar came home and Ingolf told him about this.

He replied: "I shall be pleased if this turns out well, and I shall tell you three times if my father is displeased with you. But then if you don't do anything about it I shall stop." Now Ingolf took over the job of foreman, and Glum was well satisfied with him.

One day Glum went to a horse-fighting contest with his foreman, who was riding a mare, while the stallion was running alongside. There was good sport there. Kalf of Stokkahladir was there — he had a seedy old beast which was beating every other horse. He spoke:

"Why not match that splendid animal[2] belonging to the Thvera people against mine?"

Glum replied: "That's not a fair contest — that horse and your old nag."

He said: "The reason why you don't want to must be that there's no spirit in him; perhaps the old proverb will prove true, that the livestock's like its master."

Glum replied: "You can't possibly know about that, and speaking on Ingolf's behalf I won't refuse, but the fight mustn't go on any longer than he wants it to."

Kalf said: "It's a pretty good bet that not much will be done against your wishes."

The horses were led forward and fought well, and it seemed to everyone that Ingolf's horse was getting the better of it, and then Glum decided to part them. They rode home; Ingolf was there for that year and Glum was well pleased with him.

There was a gathering beside the river in Djupadal. Glum came there, and Ingolf with his horse. Kalf came — he was a friend of the Espihol people. His horse was there, and he suggested that they should now let the horses fight to a finish. Glum said Ingolf should decide. He said he was reluctant, but that he didn't like to back out of it. The horses were led forward; Kalf beat his horse, but Ingolf's horse was on top in

---

2. *dýrkálker* — unique word; *dýr* means "animal" and *kálker* "chalice", hence "anything very valuable". Alternatively, *kálkr* might be a variant of *kjálki* – "jaw" (the reading of some paper MSS), but this is hard to make convincing sense of.

every round. Then Kalf banged his stick down across the ears of Ingolf's horse, so that it became dizzy, but immediately afterwards it returned to the attack. Then Glum went forward and restored fair play, and the end of it was that Kalf's horse left the ring. Then there was a great uproar, and at parting Kalf hit Ingolf with the stick. Now men came between them. Glum said:

"Let's pay no attention to this sort of thing — this is how every horsefight ends here."

Mar said to Ingolf: "My father certainly intends to see that no disgrace comes to you as a result of this blow."

CHAPTER 14

THERE WAS A man called Thorkel who lived at Hamar. Ingolf used to go there and visit the farmer's daughter — she was a pretty woman. Her father was wealthy but not a distinguished man. All the same, Ingolf attended well enough to the overseeing at home, though he produced less craftsmanship than he had done. Mar had a word with him about it one time: "Now I find that it annoys my father when you go away from the farm." Ingolf reassured him, but it still went on in the same way. Mar mentioned it a second and a third time, but it had no effect.

One evening when Ingolf had come home late and people had finished eating, Glum said:

"Now just for fun we'll each name what we place our trust in. I'll choose first, and there are three things I place reliance on — one is my purse, the second my axe, the third my storehouse."

Then they chose, one after the other.

Then Glum said: "Who do you choose, Ingolf?"

He answered: "Thorkel of Hamar."

Glum leapt up with his sword's hilt in front of him, stormed up to him and said:

"A fine patron you've chosen for yourself!"

Everyone saw that Glum was angry. He went out, and Ingolf with him. Then he said to Ingolf: "Now go to your patron and say that you've killed Kalf of Hladir."

He said: "why should I tell such a lie against myself?"

"You'll do as I wish."

And now they both walked on together and Glum went into the barn and saw a calf there, and "Hit it on the head," he said, "and take the bloody sword to him[1] — go south over the river now and say that your only hope of protection is with him, and show him the bloody sword so that the evidence is clear."

He did so — found Thorkel and told him the news, that he had remembered the blow that Kalf had struck him and said he had killed him — "and I am asking for protection here as you have promised."

He replied: "You're a great fool and you've killed a good fellow. Get out at once — I don't want you killed on my farm."

He went home and came to meet Glum, and he asked: "How did the patron turn out then?"

Ingolf replied: "Not too well."

Glum said: "Well, try placing reliance on me now," and went with him out into the storehouse. "You'll be in trouble if Kalf of Hladir *is* killed."

The next day the killing of Hladir-Kalf of Stokkahladir was

---

1. Literally, M.'s text means ". . . and Glum goes and saw a calf there and hits it on the head and takes the bloody sword to him" — but it is clear from the later resolution of the story that Ingolf, and not Glum, must have killed the calf. Accordingly I have emended M.'s *Ok nú víkr hann Glúmr, ok sá þar kálf einn, ok høggr í höfuðit ok fær honum sverðit blóðugt* (Turville-Petre's normalisation) to *ok nú víkr hann Glúmr í hlöðu ok sá þar kálf einn, ok "høgg þú í höfuðit", segir hann, "ok fær honum sverðit blóðugt"*, which gives the translation offered here. As the noun *hlaða* means "barn", *Hlöðu-Kálfr* can mean either "Kalf of Hladir" or "a calf in the barn".

84

announced. And now Thorkel said that someone had come to him and confessed to having committed that crime; everyone thought that the confession was true. Now that winter passed. Glum sent Ingolf north to Einar Konalsson[2] and gave him nine hundred measures of homespun[3] and said:

"You've had no wages from me, and with your prudent nature you'll be able to put this to good use. I'll take care of this case which is being brought against you, and it won't do you any harm — I saddled you with it because of your obstinacy. And if you come back to Iceland, you may visit me."

Ingolf said: "I must ask you not to allow the woman to be married to anyone else."

"I promise you that."

His mares stayed behind. Einar Konalsson arranged for Ingolf to go abroad, but Thorvald prepared the case about the killing of Kalf for the Assembly at Hegranes, and it came to the point that Ingolf was going to be outlawed. Glum was there too, as well as some relatives of Ingolf. They came to see Glum, asked for his help and said they would contribute towards the compensation for Ingolf's crime.

Glum said: "I'll settle this case without damages."

When the court convened and the defence was called, Glum said that

---

2. See ch. 9 note 7. Einar Konalsson lived at Einarsstadir in Reykjadal, some 40 km. North-East of Thvera.

3. Currency could be reckoned in standard measures of new homespun cloth; the "hundred" here = 120, so that the payment is equal to 1080 ells of homespun (about 540 English yards). The *eyrir* ("ounce") was legally six ells, and eight ounces made one mark; the "hundred" was therefore 2½ marks, and Ingolf would receive 22½ marks in homespun. The exchange rate between homespun and silver was probably 7½ to one, and this would make the payment worth 3 marks in silver (*Refsingar á Íslandi*, pp. 349–51) — or about 1½ pounds weight. This answers fairly closely to compensations for assault in other sagas — cf. particularly *Reykdæla saga* ch. 23, a case which bears a considerable resemblance to this one.

the case was invalid — "You've prepared the case for the slaying against the wrong man — and in fact I did it myself." Then he named his witnesses that the case was void. "And even if Ingolf did kill a calf in the barn, I haven't prosecuted him for it. Now I'll offer satisfaction, more in line with what the man was worth than with the pride of you people from Espihol." People went home from the Assembly.

Ingolf was abroad that winter, but was not content to stay away any longer. He sold his property and bought fine valuables and precious tapestries. Glum had given him a good cloak, which he traded for a scarlet tunic. And the summer that he went away, a man called Thjodolf returned to Iceland. His mother lived at Æsustadir. He went to Hamar and met Helga. One day Glum had ridden up to Holar and as he was riding down to Saurbær, there was Thjodolf coming towards him. Then Glum said:

"I don't like your visits to Hamar. I intend to arrange Helga's marriage myself, and if you don't leave off I shall challenge you to a duel."

He replied that he wouldn't compete against Glum, and gave up his visits.

CHAPTER 15

NOW INGOLF CAME out to Iceland and went to Thvera, and Glum received him and invited him to stay[1] with him. He accepted. One day Ingolf said: "Now Glum, I want you to look over my goods." He did so, and they seemed to him to have been a good investment. Then Ingolf said: "You gave me the means to pay for my journey; now I say this property is yours."

---

1. M. *setugrið* — a rare word, elsewhere means "peace"; but its meaning here is established by the cognate *setumenn* — "inmates", "residents".

Then Glum said: "You haven't got any property I intend to take."

"Here are some wall-hangings, anyway, which I've bought for you — you must accept those — and here is a tunic."

Glum said: "I'll accept your gifts."

One day Glum asked whether Ingolf wanted to stay in his household. Ingolf replied: "I don't intend to part from you if I have the choice of staying. I'll give you my stud mares."

Glum said: "I'll accept the mares, but now we must go and see Thorkel at Hamar today." And so they did. Thorkel gave Glum a good welcome.

Then Glum said: "You have done Ingolf an injustice, and now you must make up for it by marrying your daughter to him. He's worth this match, and I'll put down the money for his marriage portion. I've proved him to be a good fellow — and if you don't do this, you'll come to regret your mistake."

Thorkel agreed to this course of action, and Ingolf married the woman and became a farmer and a useful fellow.

CHAPTER 16
About Viga-Skuta

G LUM MARRIED HIS daughter Thorlaug to Viga-Skuta up north at Myvatn, but because the couple quarrelled Skuta sent her back home to Thvera and abandoned her. Glum was annoyed at that. Afterwards Arnor Crone Nose asked for her hand and married her, and outstanding men are descended from them. After that, there was a great feud between Glum and Skuta.[1]

One summer a vagrant came to Skuta and asked to be taken in. Skuta

---

1. A fuller account of this feud, both before and after the marriage of Skuta and Thorlaug, appears in *Reykdæla saga* chs. 23–6; cf. Turville-Petre's ed., Introduction pp. xxiii–xxxii.

asked what his trouble was. He said he had killed a man and was not safe in his own area. Skuta said: "I'm not aware of any obligation towards you, so what will you do to earn my protection?"

He said: "What are you asking for?"

Skuta said: "You are to go on an errand of mine to Viga-Glum[2] and speak to him in these terms — that you think you need him to take charge of your affairs. Now as regards your meeting, I expect that he will turn out to be riding to the Assembly. He can be relied on to help those who need him, and he may tell you to go to Thvera and wait for him there. You must say that you are in too much danger for that, and that you'd rather have the chance of talking with him alone — and then perhaps he may make some suggestion. You are to ask to be allowed to meet him in Mjadmardal,[3] which runs up from the farm buildings at Thvera and where his herdsman's bothies[4] stand; say you'd like to meet him there on a stated day." He agreed to this, and now everything went as Skuta had planned. This ruffian now came back to Skuta and told him. He said: "Then you've done your errand well. Now stay with me."

Time passed. And when the date came on which Glum had promised

---

2. "Slaying Glum"; the nickname is only given to Glum in this chapter, and it may originate with Skuta, who is given it three times in those parts of *Reykdæla saga* which have no connection with *Viga-Glums saga* (*Reykdæla saga* chs. 1, 30). But it must early have become traditional for Glum — Snorri uses it four times in *Skáldskaparmál*, written ca. 1222, (*Edda Snorra Sturlusonar*, ed. Finnur Jónsson, Copenhagen 1931) and cf. its use in the stories of Ögmund Bash and Thorvald Chatterbox.

3. M. *Miðárdalr* — "Middle river valley" (and cf. the first sentence of ch. 19), apparently the same as *Mjaðmárdalr*. The word is undecipherable in the longer version of the saga.

4. Remains of two structures, each of which might have been a sheepfold and bothy, survive on slight knolls in the lower part of Mjadmardal. These were already known as Fremri — ("Upper") and Ytri — ("Outer") Glumsstadir by 1712 (*Jarðabók Árna Magnússonar og Páls Vídalíns*, 12 vols. Copenhagen 1913–1943, Vol. X p. 289), but the names could still be due to the saga itself. Local tradition believes the nearer of the two to be the bothy of the saga, and the topography fits the description given here, but there has been no excavation of it, and its date and purpose remain uncertain.

the messenger that they should meet, Skuta set out from home with thirty men. He rode from the north westwards over Vödla Heath and onto the ridge which is called Raudahjalli.[5] There they dismounted. Then Skuta said: "You must wait here for a bit, while I ride in along the ridge to find out if there's anything to be caught."

As he pressed on up the valley, he saw a big man in a green cape riding up from Thvera, and realised that it was Glum. Then he got off his horse. He had a reversible cloak over him, one side black and the other white. He left the horse in the clearing and then walked to the bothy — and Glum had by now gone inside it. Skuta had a sword in his hand called "Fly",[6] and a helmet on his head; he went to the doorway of the bothy, banged on the wall and then moved aside close to the bothy. Glum came out with nothing in his hand, saw nobody, and turned to face the bothy. Then Skuta came between him and the doorway of the bothy. Glum recognised the man and took to his heels — and the river-gully was near the bothy.[7] Skuta called to him to wait. He replied that

5. "Red Ledge", now lost, apparently a cleft in the ridge above Kaupang. There are two such paths, but one is too easy of access to provide a defensive position, the other so difficult that Skuta could hardly have got his horse back up it, and not worth defending, since it joins the other at the top of the slope. Jónas Kristjánsson concludes that the author didn't know the area very well, but cf. note 7.

6. The related *Reykdæla saga* ch. 26 expresses doubt as to whether it was a sword or an axe, and in chs. 20 and 22 calls it an axe.

7. The distance is some two hundred yards. Jónas Kristjánsson argues that Glum would not have jumped over the cliff edge, because there is an easier descent near it and Skuta would have seen him on the ledge — and hence that the writer was not familiar with the detailed geography. But Glum could have thrown his cloak down into the river from the ledge, and between it and the easier descent is an outcrop of rock which would probably conceal Glum from Skuta. However the Mjadma river is not usually deep enough for a man to swim in it, so that Skuta could not have mistaken the cloak for Glum; and Glum could hardly have reclimbed the scree-strewn slope without attracting Skuta's attention by the noise. Jónas rightly adds that Skuta could easily have escaped while Glum was gathering his men; but these are all failures of imagination rather than of information, and the author of this chapter probably knew the area well.

he would think that a fair request if they were equally well armed. Glum ran to the gully and Skuta pursued. Glum plunged down over the edge, but Skuta looked for a way down where it was possible to walk, saw the cape drifting in the river at the bottom, rushed to the spot and immediately thrust at it. Then he heard a voice above him:

"Not much credit in spoiling people's clothes." Skuta looked up and recognised Glum there. He had known, in fact, that there was a grassy ledge underneath the point where he had gone over.

Then Skuta said: "Now you've got this to remember, Glum, that you've run away and not dared wait for Skuta."

Glum said: "That's true, but I intend you to run just as far before the sun sets this evening."

Then Glum recited a verse:

3.   It's worth a piece of silver
     Each bush south of the river —
     The wide woods often cover
     Outlaw and wolf together.[8]

With that they parted for the time being. Glum went home, gathered his men and told about the trap that had been set for him; he said too that he wanted it quickly repaid. In a short time he got together sixty men, and they rode up into the valley. Skuta walked to his horse when he and Glum had parted and rode along the hillside, and now he saw the party of riders and knew that it would do him no good to meet them, so he resorted to a trick — broke his spearhead off and used the shaft as a staff, took off the saddle and rode bareback, turned his cloak inside out and rode towards the sheep shouting loudly. They came up and asked if

---

8. The lower Mjadma river runs almost north and south, but the further bank is slightly the more southerly. Yet to hide from Skuta and get back to Thvera, Glum must reclimb the *near* side of the gully. This verse may therefore be taken from some other context, or else the reference is to the Thvera river – see map 3.

he'd seen an imposing man riding past the hill with weapons. He said he had.

They asked: "What's your name?"

He replied: "I am called "Many" in the Myvatn area, but "Few" in the district around Kaupang."

They said: "You choose to answer us with taunts and mockery". He said he didn't know how to say anything truer, and parted from them. And as soon as they were gone he took his weapons and saddle and rode at full speed towards his men.

They found Glum and told him that they'd met a man who answered them with mockery, and said what he had called himself. "Now that showed a lack of brains," said Glum. "It was Skuta you met there, and what could he have said that was truer? Because around Myvatn there are many caves, but in the Kaupang district[9] in Eyjafjord there's not a cave to be found; we nearly had him there, so we'll go on riding after him."

They came to the ridge, and Skuta and his men had got there first. But there is a path there wide enough for only one person, and it's a position which is easier to defend with thirty men than to attack with sixty. Then Skuta said: "Now you've gone to a lot of trouble to chase me. Perhaps you reckon you've got to get your own back for having run away, and that was a brave deed of yours to jump into the gully. You weren't slow then!"

Glum said: "That's true. You knew how to be afraid too, when you pretended to be shepherd to the people of Eyjafjord and hid your weapons — except for the ones you broke. I don't think you ran any less far than I did."

"However it's gone so far, you just attack now with twice the men I've got."

---

9. *Fiskilækjarhverfi*, "Fishbrooks district", a name for the district surrounding Kaupang at the head of Eyjafjord — a flattish, marshy area. The name Skuta means "cave", of which the dramatic volcanic landscape round Myvatn has a large number.

Glum said: "I think we'll part now for the time being, whatever is thought of it on either side."

Now Skuta rode north and Glum back home to Thvera.[10]

CHAPTER 17
About Viga-Glum's children

WHEN THORIR DIED, Thorarin set up a farm at North Espihol and lived there. Glum had children with his wife. One of his sons was called Mar, as has been mentioned, and the other Vigfus. Both were promising, but they were completely unlike each other. Mar was quiet and prudent, but Vigfus a very boisterous person, an unscrupulous man, of great strength and full of courage. There was a man in Glum's household called Hallvard, his freedman and Vigfus's foster father. He was raking in money and was a fox in financial matters. He entrusted his money to Vigfus. He wasn't popular. He set up house on the farm called Tjörn, high up in Eyjafjord valley, and his popularity didn't improve with that, for he was just as much of a thief in the pastures. But Vigfus was very much the sea-going merchant.

A man called Halli lived at Jorunnarstadir, who was known as Halli the White. He was the son of Thorbjörn, and his mother was called Vigdis. She was the daughter of Audun the Bald.[1] He had fostered Einar Eyjolfsson,[2] who had then come into possession of Saurbær. Halli was blind; he was concerned with all the arbitrations arranged in the district, because he was both wise and just. His sons were Orm and Brusi the

---

10. M. makes this the first sentence of ch. 17, but all editors have regarded it as the end of this chapter, where it seems rather to belong.

1. *rotinn* — usually "rotten", but used specifically of hides from which the hair has fallen off through rottenness, hence "bald".

Poet, who both lived at Torfufell, and Bard, who lived at Skaldsstadir. Bard was a turbulent and very unscrupulous man and better than anyone at fighting, hasty in speech and inclined to be abusive. He was married to Una, daughter of Oddkel of Thjorsardal.

One autumn ten or twelve wethers belonging to Halli the White went missing from the pasture and couldn't be found. And when Bard and his father met, Halli asked what he supposed had become of his wethers. Bard said: "I'm not surprised at sheep disappearing when there are thieves living next door — since Hallvard came to these parts, that is."

Halli said: "I want you to prepare a case against him and summon him for theft, and I don't expect Glum to produce a jury verdict in his favour if I have a theft case brought against him."

Bard said: "It'll be hard to get a verdict that goes against Vigfus and his father."

CHAPTER 18

NOW BARD BROUGHT the case, and when Vigfus heard about it he told his father that it wouldn't please him to have a charge of theft brought against his foster father.

Glum replied: "You know he's unreliable, and it will be an unpopular business to get him acquitted."

Vigfus said: "I could wish the dispute was about something more serious."

Glum replied: "It would seem to me better to pay compensation on

---

2. Einar later became known as Einar of Thvera. He and his brother Gudmund were often on opposing sides, and although *Viga-Glums saga* portrays them as allies, *Ljósvetninga saga* ch. 6 says that their enmity had begun while they were boys and was still going on after Einar had come to Thvera. Other sources associate Saurbær with Hlenni the Old (eg. *Njáls saga* ch. 105), but this probably refers to the period after Einar's move to Thvera.

his behalf and to let him come here and give up his farm, rather than pledge my reputation for a man like that."

Now people came to the Assembly and the case into court, and it was up to Glum to deliver the verdict with a jury. Then Vigfus realised that he intended to pronounce Hallvard guilty, and he went into the court and said that if his foster father became an outlaw he would want to make Glum pay dearly for it. And the result was that Glum dismissed the case and acquitted him, and was discredited by doing so.

But when a year or two had passed after that, Halli lost a home-fattened boar so fat that it could hardly get up. Then Bard came one day and asked if the boar had been slaughtered. Halli said it was lost.

Bard replied:[1] "It must have gone to look for the sheep that were stolen the other autumn."

He said: "I reckon they've gone the same way; will you want to summon Hallvard?"

Bard replied: "That's what we must do, because Glum won't acquit him now, since Vigfus caused the acquittal last time, and now he's out of the country."

Bard took on the case and went to serve the summons. And when he met Hallvard he brought his case to a prompt conclusion by chopping his head off. Afterwards he told his father. Halli was displeased and immediately went to see Glum, told him what had happened and offered him a settlement on his own terms. Glum accepted that, stipulated a small sum, and caused payment to be made for the boar and the sheep; and that won general approval. But when Vigfus returned to Iceland, he was annoyed about the killing of Hallvard. Glum said: "I won't allow this settlement that's been made now to be broken." Now Bard and Vigfus had no dealings with each other even when they happened to meet.

The next summer a horse-fighting contest was arranged at which all

---

1. M. omits "replied", an obvious scribal error.

the stallions available in the area were to compete. Those from the upper and lower districts of the valley were to oppose each other, and each side had to choose a man to say which horses had won; the verdict of those who were chosen was to be final. From the upper district Bard was chosen, and from the lower district Vigfus Glumsson. There was a large number of horses there and the sport was good, with a very close contest, and many bouts were seen in the course of the day. The end of it was that equal numbers had fought well and run away on both sides, and they agreed to call it a draw. But then Vigfus said he had a horse which had not fought — "and it's the best that's come here today; you bring one in against it."

Bard replied: "It looks vicious to us; we won't bring one against it, but we'll still call it a draw."

Vigfus said: "So you haven't got one, and you just don't want it said that you were no match for us."

"You've been properly impartial so far, but now your judgement's getting a bit clouded, and it's becoming clear that you must have stood by the larder shelves and discussed the cooking with your mother more often than you've been to horsefights — that's what it looks like from your pretty little blonde beard, anyway."[2]

Vigfus laughed at that, and so did many others. Halli's serving man came home and he asked about the horse-fighting contest. The servant said:

"They decided it was a draw."

Halli asked: "Were Bard and Vigfus agreed?"

He replied: "Well enough, though Bard made one remark at Vigfus's expense."

He asked what that was, and the servant told him.

---

2. Literally "the colour of your beard is that way". Bard means that Vigfus's beard is effeminate in colour (blonde, milky, cf. *ljóss/hvítr matr*, literally "light/white food" — "dairy food", and the English "milksop").

Halli said: "That bodes ill."

The serving man said: "Vigfus laughed at it."

Halli replied: "It's the custom of him and his father to laugh when the killing mood is on them."

Father and son met, and Halli asked Bard what had possessed him to say anything so outrageous — "and I fear it may lead to great misfortune. The only thing for it is for you to go abroad to get yourself wood for house building — and stay abroad for three years, otherwise you've had it."

Bard replied: "It wouldn't matter[3] if you weren't a coward. That's what old age does — makes you afraid for your son."

Halli said: "You may be a great hero, but it will be difficult for you to protect yourself in the district."

Bard followed his father's advice and went abroad. Later, Halli paid a vagrant to go into Skagafjord and west from there and put it about that Bard had gone abroad because he didn't dare, in the face of Vigfus and his father, to do other than go into exile for a single word, and that nobody dared do anything against them in the district. He did as Halli told him. This trick was carried out so that Bard's relatives might not be molested because of him. Bard stayed abroad for a year, and then came back to his farm.

---

3. M. *Ekki lag væri at* is of uncertain meaning; this translation assumes an extension of meaning in *lag* from "value" to "importance". Jónas Kristjánsson (*Íslenzk fornrit* IX p. 62) suggests the sarcastic meaning "There'd be something wrong if you weren't a coward", or that, removing the negative, the sense might be "It would be alright if...".

CHAPTER 19

The Fall of Bard the White

HALLI HAD BEEN looking after Bard's farm while he was abroad, and had had some timber felled in a wood in Mjadmardal which belonged to Bard. Bard had also brought a lot of wood back with him. He was sometimes at his own farm, sometimes with his father. Bard said he wanted to fetch his timber. Halli said: "I'd rather you didn't go yourself, and it's not good to trust to that man and his father."

Bard said nobody would know about their journey. He went with a serving man to fetch the timber, and they had a large number of horses. But his wife Una had gone to Vidines to see her sister Oddkatla, and Bard came there, and Hlenni offered to get another man to go to the wood while Bard stayed there — he thought that would be more prudent. Bard said there was no need for that.

The sisters went with him out of the farmstead; but as they were returning, Una looked back towards him over her shoulder and fell in a faint. When she regained consciousness, her sister asked what she had seen. "I saw dead men[1] going to meet Bard, and he must be fated to die, and we shall never see each other again."

Now Bard and his man went on, and a mist came down as they entered the wood, and they tied the timber in bundles and hobbled the horses. Early that morning the shepherd from Thvera was up and about. It often happened that Vigfus met the shepherd and asked for news, and so it was that morning; and he said: "It's remarkable that you always

---

1. Visions of dead men were commonly held to presage death for the person they came to fetch — cf. for example *Atlamál* st. 25, *Gísla saga* ch. 30; cf. ch. 9 note 1.

find the sheep in such darkness. I should never find sheep in such a fog."

He replied: "It wasn't difficult for me to find the sheep. The men I saw in the woods this morning had more trouble finding their horses — and they were standing right beside them. But they looked pleased with themselves all the same, and one of them was in a green tunic and had a shield by his side."

Vigfus asked if he had recognised the man. He said he thought it would be Bard — "because he owns the wood they were in."

Vigfus said: "Fetch three of my horses."

There were two Norwegians staying there; Vigfus asked them to ride with him, and said he was going to the baths. He turned south from the farmstead across Laugardal.[2] Then the Norwegians said: "Where do you want to go now?"

He replied: "On my own business first" — and he rode a good way in front of them. They went south, riding above the farmland there until they saw Bard coming out of the woods with his work horses. Bard's servant saw the pursuit and spoke. "These men behind are riding hard," he said.

"What of it?" said Bard.

He replied: "That's Vigfus, and I should like us to ride away — there's no disgrace in it so long as we don't know what they want."

Bard said: "Vigfus won't attack me with two other men provided you're not with me."

He replied: "I'd rather stay with the horses, and that you went to Vidines; there's no shame in your riding to a place where you have business, and besides, you don't know for certain what the men behind us are after. And Hlenni told you not to trust them."

Bard said: "You must ride on ahead and raise the alarm if my arrival is delayed longer than one might expect, because there won't be any

---

2. "Baths Valley" or "Hot Springs Valley"; the name is lost, but there are two hot springs a little to the south of Thvera, and probably Thverardal is meant.

quick conclusion between me and Vigfus if the two of us are to fight it out. And he's too good a fellow to attack me with two other men, but if we are two and they three, then they'll make use of the difference."

Now he did as Bard ordered, but Bard unfastened his shield and made himself ready as best he could. And when they met, Bard asked what their business might be. Vigfus said that they wouldn't both go away from that meeting alive; and Bard said he was ready if the two of them were to face each other, "but there's no courage in three attacking one." Then the Norwegians said they would have stayed at home if they had known the purpose, and declared that they still couldn't give any support unless men came[3] to help Bard, since his companion had fled. Vigfus told them to wait and see first how things went. After that he and Bard fought for a long time and neither was wounded, but Vigfus was getting so much the worst of it that he had repeatedly to give ground before he could get into a position to strike. Bard had his sword and defended himself extremely well and wasn't wounded at all. It seemed to the Norwegians that it would be a great disaster if Vigfus was laid low while they stood by, and if men then came to support Bard. So then they rushed at Bard and killed him, and he was dead by the time Hlenni and his men arrived.[4]

But Vigfus and his companions rode home, and Glum showed anger at what had been done, and said that great trouble had been started in the area. Halli went to see his foster son Einar at Saurbær and asked him to take on the case. He said he was bound to prosecute the case for his kinsman and foster brother. After that they rode to see Thorarin and asked him for support. Thorarin said he couldn't think of anyone he'd rather be associated with, and vowed his friendship to them both over this case and every other.

---

3. M. "if men came", but the sense is clearly defective, and a negative is added by recent editors.

4. M. omits the verb. For the discovery of what may be Bard's grave, see Introduction p. 15.

Matters went to the Assembly and an attempt was made at reconciliation, but such was the opposition that there was no chance of that, because there were skilful lawyers and bold men on the other side, the men of Mödrufell and Espihol. This case ended with the Norwegians being completely outlawed and payment made for Vigfus to be allowed merely exile; and he was to have three years to find a passage abroad and meanwhile to be allowed three places of safety each year, and that made him a lesser outlaw. But he could not remain at home because of the sanctity of the place. He was at Uppsalir for a long time, and people thought he must be in another quarter of the country, but he wouldn't go abroad in the time allowed. He then became a complete outlaw, and Glum maintained him secretly. But outlawed men were not supposed to be there, because Frey, to whom the temple there was dedicated, did not allow it. Thus six years passed.

CHAPTER 20

About the foster brothers

N OW WE MUST take up the story when the foster brothers Arngrim and Steinolf grew up. When Thorgrim of Mödrufell died Arngrim went to his farm, and Steinolf with him, and there was still as much affection between them as there had ever been. Arngrim took a wife and married Thordis, daughter of Björn and sister of Arnor Crone Nose.[1] Steinolf used to travel as a merchant, but stayed with Arngrim when he was in Iceland.

---

1. Arnor *kerlingarnef* was a chieftain in Skagafjord, the next major valley to the west of Eyjafjord, and a short story about him survives in the "Great" *saga of Olaf Tryggvason* ch. 226 (ed. Ólafur Halldórsson, 2 vols. *Editiones Arnamagnæanae*, Series A, 1–2, Copenhagen 1958–61, II 180–4). His peculiar nickname may indicate that he had a hooked nose.

One summer when he arrived in Eyjafjord, Arngrim didn't invite him to stay with him, didn't speak to him even though they met, and gave it as his reason that Steinolf had had more to do with his wife Thordis than was proper; but most people's view is that there was little or nothing in it. Then Glum invited him to stay with him, and that's how it was for some years, that he stayed with Glum when he was in Iceland, and there was a cordial relationship between them. Steinolf was a very gifted man. One summer Glum did not invite him and said that he wanted him to be at Uppsalir with his father — "and the reason why I don't invite you is that I disapprove of having people to stay. But if you're with your father you'll come over to Thvera and I'll be pleased to see you." So it went on for some years, that Vigfus was at Uppsalir with Arnor Red Cheek while he was outlawed, and Steinolf was there too.

One autumn the farmer at Öxnafell was holding his daughter's wedding and invited to it all the most important inhabitants of Eyjafjord. Steinolf was also invited; he came to Thvera and wanted to go with Glum. Glum said he wasn't going. Steinolf said: "I take a poor view of you being loose with your word."[2]

Glum replied: "Less harm will come of my careless words than of your recklessness, and I'm not going there. A fine thing," said Glum, "for a mere peasant to invite so many powerful men to his house, and I hope no treachery follows. I have a suspicion about the motive for this invitation; the farmer isn't doing it on his own initiative, and it seems to me better that my friends shouldn't go."

Steinolf went to the feast, as did all those who were invited except Glum. Einar Eyjolfsson and Thorvald and Arngrim[3] talked much together. On the day people were due to depart, Einar made a long speech about the management of the district and said it was always fitting when

---

2. Perhaps we are to assume that Glum had earlier said he would go and then changed his mind. The obscurity could be due to the compression of the saga in M.

3. M. *Steingrim* — an obvious scribal mistake, confusing the names Arngrim and Steinolf.

large numbers of people came together that there should be some discussion of those matters that most needed it at the time and might be improved. "And for a long time there has been a dispute between two proud men — I refer to the kinsmen, Arngrim and Steinolf. There has been ill feeling between them, but we believe it was based on lies and the words of malicious people. Now Arngrim is willing to invite Steinolf to stay with him, and he'll give him a good reception if he's prepared to accept, so have done with your unfriendliness, both of you."

Steinolf said he was very willing, declared that he knew of no cause for complaint against him, and said that of all men he was most fond of Arngrim. After that each person went back to his own home, but Steinolf went with Arngrim, stayed there for a few nights and was splendidly entertained.

CHAPTER 21

The fall of Steinolf

ONE DAY ARNGRIM asked Steinolf if he would like to go drinking with him[1] down at Grund and spend two or three nights there. He replied: "I'll go home for the meantime and come to visit you again when you're at home." Arngrim said he'd like him to wait there for him if he didn't want to go with him. Now Arngrim went to Grund, while Steinolf stayed behind at Mödrufell overnight. But next morning Steinolf was sitting by the fire and had a bit of repair work in hand — it

---

1. *skytningr* (from *skot* — "a contribution", "payment"); there is plenty of evidence for inn-like establishments in Norway, but this is the only surviving reference which may suggest one in Iceland. It may have been a centre at which imported liquor could be obtained, but one would not then expect it to be as far up the valley as Grund, but rather near Gásar, the likely port of arrival. It was perhaps more probably a drinking party in which each man paid his share of the cost.

was some little casket which belonged to the lady of the house. At that moment Arngrim came home along with Thorvald Hook, and as they came into the kitchen Steinolf was bending down. Then Arngrim struck at his head so that he was killed instantly. Then Thordis went up to him and said: "Damn you for your blow! This is the doing of cleverer men than you, but from this day onwards I shall never be your wife." Now she went to her brother Arnor Crone Nose and never again came into the same bed as Arngrim, and said before she rode away: "The reward for this, Arngrim, will be that you won't live long, for your future days will be worse than your past." And afterwards Asgrim son of Ellida-Grim married her.

Arngrim and Thorvald rode to Espihol, told Thorarin the news and asked him for protection, saying that they had neither the wits nor the popularity to stand up to Glum themselves, while Thorarin was both wise and popular. He answered that the deed seemed a bad one to him and he was afraid no good would come of it. Thorvald said it was no use blaming oneself for what was done, and said he thought Thorarin would soon have to get to grips with more serious trouble if he gave them no protection; but they said perhaps supporters could be got if he spoke up on their behalf.

Thorarin said: "My advice is that you move your households here, both from Grund and Mödrufell, and we'll gather men as quickly as possible and combine our households before Glum realises what's happening." They did so before Glum heard about it. And when he found out, he gathered a force and proceeded against them at once; but nothing was gained by that, because the people at Espihol were more numerous. And they sat quiet throughout the winter. But Glum was never outwitted[2] that winter; he was so much on his guard that he was never to be found in the bed that had been prepared for him. He often

---

2. M. has omitted a word here — modern editors add *unninn* — "overcome" (ie. "got the better of", "outwitted").

slept little at night, and he and Mar used to walk about discussing legal proceedings. One night Mar asked how he had slept. Glum recited a verse:

4. I do not sleep easy,
  Warrior with Odin's bowstring,
  Safe on this farm, nor shall they,
  Though blazing with sea gold, find me easily paid,
  Till against shield gates blazing,
  The sword resounds on "hat-mountain"
  (And often I've slain for less)
  Till over some of their heads it screams some more.[3]

"Now I must tell you my dream; I dreamt I was walking away from the farmstead here, alone and unarmed, but Thorarin was walking towards me with a large whetstone in his hand, and I thought I was ill prepared for our encounter. And when I thought about it, I saw another whetstone beside me, and I went towards him with it. And when we met, each tried to hit the other, but the stones collided with a loud crash."

Mar asked: "Did you think that might be a sign of our household crashing down?"[4]

Glum said: "It was too big for that."

"Did you think it might mean the district crashing down?"

Glum replied: "It might well be compared with that, for I dreamed of being aware that it was heard throughout the district. And when I woke up, I recited a verse:"

---

3. Prose sense: "I shall not go to sleep peacefully on the farm, warrior — it won't be easy for the wealthy men to compensate me — before the sword resounds again on some of their heads. Often I've killed a man for less."

4. *hýbýlabrestr* — *brestr* usually means "a loud noise", but here rather "calamity" — cf. *Gísla saga* II, ch. 2. referring to the loss to a family through the death of one of its members, and *heimsbrestr* ("a world calamity") in *Njáls saga* ch. 156. On this and other examples of "punning" in dreams in Old Norse, see Turville-Petre ed. p. 76.

5.   With a whetstone the keeper of bear-cubs,
        The oarsman of cubs of the fjord,
        As I watched in my dream, the warrior
        Like a wave-god heaved it and struck me.
        But then I thought with a grindstone
        That goaded by anger, I smote him,
        The sea-charger's horseman, I struck him,
        Deft in my sleep its steersman I hit with a whetstone.[5]

Mar said it was likely that the old saying would come true "that each of you will hit the other with a sore stone before all's done".

Glum replied: "Such a thing is not unlikely — there are a lot of strange signs to suggest it. But there's another dream to tell you. I dreamt I was standing outside, and I saw two women. They had a trough between them, and they stopped at Hrisateig[6] and from there sprinkled blood over the whole district. And after that I woke up, and I think that foreshadows something important." And he recited a verse:

6.   The giver of rings saw them riding,
        And a grinding of swords comes towards us;
        It's come, the grey spears' greeting,
        At last, with the gods through the pasture;
        Where the biting goddesses sprinkled
        Men's blood at the meeting of edges,

---

5. Prose sense: "The tough warrior struck me with a whetstone — I saw that in my dream. But I dreamt that, spurred on by anger, I struck the bold steersman with a whetstone." This verse owes its main image to the mythical struggle between Thor and the giant Hrungnir, in which part of a whetstone lodged in Thor's head (cf. *Myth and Religion of the North* pp. 76–8).

6. "Brushwood meadow" — the name is now lost, but from ch. 22 it is clearly the strip of meadow on the east bank of the Eyjafjord river which stretches southwards towards the ford.

While Odin, death's ally, exulted,
In slaughter they dripped forth gore.[7]

That morning Mar went to Mödrufell with seventeen other men to summon Arngrim for the killing, but Glum stayed at home with five men and told them to come back quickly. Jödur stayed at home with Glum, and so did Eyjolf, son of Thorleif the Tall, Glum's nephew Thorvald Chatterbox and two slaves.

CHAPTER 22

The battle of Hrisateig

GLUM'S SISTER HELGA, who had been married to Steingrim of Sigluvik, had then come to Laugaland. She was the mother of Thorvald Chatterbox, and he was now eighteen years old. There was a man called Thorvard,[1] the son of Örnolf and of Yngvild who was nicknamed Everyone's Sister. He lived at Kristnes; his twelve-year-old son was called Gudbrand. Thorvard was a clever man, old now and not particularly well intentioned. He was up and about early that morning, and told the lad to catch some horses. Then they rode to Thvera, and when they got there Mar had just left. Glum greeted Thorvard politely, and the latter asked whether any attempt had been made at reconciliation. Glum said it hadn't.

---

7. Prose sense: "(I), the generous patron saw a great band of gods ride through the pasture — there will be a clash of swords, the grey spears' greeting has come — where the valkyries eager for slaughter sprinkled blood over men's bodies; Odin delights in it."
1. M. has *Thorvald* for the first two occurrences of the name, *Thorvard* thereafter. The latter is right — cf. *Landnámabók*, and *Reykdæla saga* chs. 15, 16. On his father Örnolf, cf. ch. 10 note 2 above; his mother got her nickname from the fact that both her parents had children by previous marriages — see Genealogical Table 2.

Thorvard said: "Is the case prepared?"

Glum said it wasn't.

"A day like this would be very suitable for delivering the summons. There's a thick mist and it wouldn't become known if one moved quietly."

Then Glum said what was happening and that there were only six men at home.

Thorvard said: "You're rather short-handed, but the plan you've adopted should do well enough all the same."

Now Thorvard rode to Espihol, and they hadn't got up when he and Gudbrand got there. He met Thorarin and asked: "What course do you intend to take? Are you going to offer Glum any settlement in the case for the killing?"

Thorarin answered: "We think it's an awkward matter, offering any settlement to Glum."

Thorvard said: "Has the prosecution for the killing been prepared?"

Thorarin replied: "I haven't heard — what do you know about it?"

He said: "Mar went to begin the proceedings this morning with seventeen men, but Glum stayed at home with five men, and now there would be a fine chance of putting your grievances right; and the reason you have so little success is because you don't react as quickly as Glum."

Thorarin replied: "I'm not going to allow any trivial charges to be put forward to counter this one."

Thorvard said: "It has to be considered whether or not there was some provocation before Steinolf was killed. Didn't he seduce Arngrim's wife? I think a case like that can hardly be thought trivial."

Thorarin replied: "I'd think it a bad thing to proceed with a charge like that."

He said: "What sort of talk is this? Glum didn't do so badly out of it when he got your relative Sigmund outlawed, and the only possible course now is to stop yourselves being disgraced like this."

Thorarin said: "I wouldn't be sure about that being a good plan."

Then people got up, and Thorvald Hook urged them to ride to Uppsalir and summon Steinolf as having been outside the protection of the law.

Thorarin replied: "That isn't advisable, but we'll do it nonetheless."

There were twenty-five[2] of them altogether, of whom seven are named — Thorarin; Thorvald Hook and his son Ketill; Arngrim; Eystein[3] the berserk; Thord Rafnsson, who lived at Stokkahladir and was married to Vigdis, Thorir's daughter, who had previously been the wife of Sigmund; and Eyvind[4] the Norwegian, who was staying with Thord. Now they went to Uppsalir, while Thorvard went to Öngulsstadir where a good farmer called Halli the Fat lived; but he sent his son to Thvera with orders to tell Glum the intention of the Espihol men — "and afterwards ride hard to meet me." But when Thorvard came to Öngulsstadir, Halli asked what news he had to tell.

"None yet," he said.

Later he told Halli what had happened, and Halli thought he saw some probability that Thorvard had brought it all about. He said such men were the cause of great misfortune and that Thorvard wanted everyone to be at loggerheads with each other — "and you deserve to be killed." Halli set off in a hurry with all the people he could get, men and women,

2. M. has xv — "fifteen", which is retained in all editions but must be a mistake. In ch. 23 the two sides have equal numbers; at that point Glum has lost three men (Thorvald Chatterbox and the two slaves) out of twenty-six (seven who began the fight, including himself and Gudbrand; eighteen reinforcements including Mar; and Vigfus) — he therefore has twenty-three men left. At the same time, the men of Espihol have had two casualties (Arngrim and Eystein), so that if they then have twenty-three men, they must have begun with twenty-five. The scribe of M. has probably omitted an x from the Roman numeral.

3. The name Eystein is omitted by M., but appears later in the chapter and in the list of casualties in ch. 23 — he is otherwise unknown; on his nickname, see ch. 4 note 2.

4. M. *Eystein*, probably as a result of the omission noted in note 3; again, the list of casualties clarifies the position. Eyvind is unknown elsewhere.

with the intention of going between the two sides if necessary.

Gudbrand came to Thvera and said his father had sent him there; he told Glum the news — "and my father said he was bound in friendship to tell you something that concerns you, namely that the men of Espihol intend to summon Steinolf as outside the law."

Glum said: "Why didn't your father come himself?"

He replied: "I would say it was all one which of us came."

Glum said: "Your father did well to send you here, since we need men."

He took the boy out of the saddle and tethered his horse.

Then Gudbrand said: "My father said I was to hurry home."

Glum replied: "Not at all. Your father would rather you showed your courage today."

Now Thorvard remarked: "My son Gudbrand is late."

Halli said: "Where did he go?"

Thorvard replied: "I sent him to Thvera."

Halli said: "It'll be a good thing if you've run up against somebody else who's crafty — it's what you deserve."

The Espihol men rode across the river; Glum had been watching their progress, and they were intending to cross over at the Kvarna ford. Then Glum said that Mar was rather late. After that he ran out of the farmstead after them, and so did those who were with him, six men including Gudbrand. Glum had his shield and battle-spear and his sword at his belt, and ran along the path towards their route with his men behind him. And when Thorarin saw him coming he gave instructions that they should ride on their way, neither faster nor slower — "and we can't be blamed for that." Thord Hrafnsson asked Thorarin if they were going to allow themselves to be chased by Glum when they had a score of men "even though he's one of only half a dozen."

Thorarin replied:[5] "We'll ride on, because Glum wants to delay us and

---

5. M. omits *svaraði* — "replied".

thus wait for his men."

Thord said: "No wonder we're worsted by Glum so often when he and you have equal forces, seeing you don't dare to wait for him even now, when he's only got a few men. And he's not going to make me run away" — and he dismounted. Eystein the berserk said he wasn't going to ride away — "and have them say they routed us."

Thorarin said: "This seems ill-advised to me."

But when Glum saw that they'd stopped, he went more slowly and addressed Thorarin, asking what their business might be at Uppsalir. Thorarin said they'd summoned Steinolf as outside the law.

Then Glum said: "Isn't that pushing things rather far? Is there to be no offer of compensation, so that we can have some discussion about how the case can be settled?"

Thorarin saw that Glum wanted to delay them and told his men to ride on, and they did so.

Glum called out: "Wait a bit."[6] But they moved off, and the slower they went, the slower Glum went, waiting for his men. And he said: "Your case won't be popular if you make lying accusations, and then there'll be disgrace for you in it."

"It won't go like that; it's difficult to have any dealings with you."

Glum got up ahead of them and engaged them in talk like this, while they rode on and he delayed them in this way. But when he saw that it was impossible to delay them further, and knew that his own men could be expected soon, he hurled his spear at Arngrim, and it went through both the saddlebow and the thigh; and Arngrim couldn't do much fighting that day. Then Eystein rushed towards Glum before anyone else,

---

6. Recent editors print M.'s text here as *við hokið þér*, which is probably the best emendation, but M. actually reads *við hok¹þat*. Northern Icelandic dialect uses *hoka við* to mean "to stop briefly". It could be a question, or an imperative plural: "Wait a bit" (assuming that *spurði* — "asked" is a mistake for *sagði* — "said", arising from wrong expansion of the abbreviation s., commonly used for both).

and Thorvald Chatterbox went against him, and the two of them struggled against each other, and those who were furthest away from their encounter were thought to be best off. Both of them were brave and physically strong; each dealt the other many and hard blows. Thorvald Hook and many others with him attacked Glum vigorously, but Glum and the men who had been following him retreated and defended themselves. Thorarin, though, did not dismount; he thought they were many enough already against one.

CHAPTER 23

Battle at Hrisateig

A MAN CAME running to where they were fighting, who was dressed in a leather cloak and had a sword in his hand. He arrived just as Thorvald Chatterbox fell before Eystein and immediately rushed at the latter and struck him a fatal blow. After that he joined Glum's force, and then Glum said this: "Welcome, Thundarbenda;[1] it was a good bargain when I bought you — today you'll repay well what you cost." Glum had a slave of that name, and that was why he said this, but in fact the man was his son Vigfus, and few or none but Glum recognised him, because he had been outlawed and in hiding for three years, and most people thought he had gone abroad. It happened while Glum was retreating that he fell, and his slaves both lay down on top of him and were stabbed to death with spears there. But at that moment Mar arrived with his men. Then Thorarin dismounted, and he and Mar fought, with no one else taking part in the struggle between them. But

---

1. This name, unrecorded elsewhere, is usually interpreted "sign of Thund (Odin)". Jónas Kristjánsson (*Íslenzk fornrit* IX p. 77) points out that *benda* in compounds usually means "bond", and "bond of Odin" is perhaps a possible if fanciful name for a slave.

Glum sprang up and fought on undaunted, and there was then no difference in numbers between the two sides.

There was a servant of Thorarin's called Eirik who was out at his work that morning — he had no shield or weapon. He took a wooden club in his hand and went to help Thorarin, and Glum's force suffered great injury from him, for men and shields were damaged by the club he had to fight with.

It's said that Halldora, Glum's wife, summoned up her women, "and we'll bind up the wounds of those who can be expected to live, whichever side they're on." But as she arrived, Thorarin fell before Mar, and his shoulder was cut open so that the lungs fell out through the wound. But Halldora bound up his wound and sat over him until the battle was finished.

Halli the Fat was the first to intervene, and many people came with him. And when the battle ended five of the men of Espihol had fallen — Thorvald Hook, Arngrim, Eystein, Eirik and Eyvind the Norwegian. And on Glum's side the casualties were Thorvald Chatterbox, Eyjolf Thorleifsson,[2] Jödur and the two slaves.

Thorarin went home with his companions. Glum also went home with his men and had the dead carried into an outbuilding, and Thorvald was treated with the greatest of care, because he was laid on cloth and sewn up in hide. But after they'd come home, Glum said to Halldora: "Our expedition would have gone well today if you'd stayed at home, and Thorarin wouldn't have got away alive."

She replied that Thorarin had little hope of recovery, "but you may be able to stay in the district for some little time even if he lives — but if he dies, you'll never be able to live at peace in Iceland again."

Then Glum said to Gudbrand: "You've won great fame today by laying low Thorvald Hook, and you were a great help to us."

He replied that it hadn't been like that, and he'd only defended himself.

---

2. M. *Rolleifsson*, but for the correct form see the end of ch. 21.

Glum said: "I saw clearly what happened — a mere child, yet you slew a champion like Thorvald, and you'll become famous for this deed. I was honoured for the same thing abroad, when I slew the berserk."

He replied: "I didn't kill Thorvald."

Glum said: "This isn't something to hide, kinsman. You gave him the wound that killed him. Don't shrink away from your good fortune." He argued with Gudbrand so much that the latter came to believe it, and admitted it and thought it a credit to him. He couldn't conceal the fact that this was disbelieved, but the killing was announced as his work, and then people thought there was less to be got out of it than had been expected by those who chose Thorvald as the man whose case they would pursue.

They say Glum remarked: "I don't think much of Mar allowing himself to be bandaged just because he's got a little graze[3] on his head." The wound he referred to like this had burst open crosswise.

Mar said: "I wouldn't need it so much if I'd lain down and used my slaves as a shield."

Then Glum spoke: "Hrisateig was hard to mow[4] today, lads," he said.

Mar said: "It will turn out to have been hard for you to mow, because now you'll have mowed the land at Thvera right out of your hands."

Glum said: "I think you can't know that with certainty."

Mar replied: "Perhaps I don't know, but it'll turn out for you as if I did."

---

3. *hnekkistikill*, used of bruises and other wounds caused by a blunt instrument. Perhaps derived from *hnekkja* — "to drive back", or *hnakki* — "the back of the head", and *stikill* — "the pointed end of a horn", it may originally have been used for a horn-handled staff, and hence for the sort of wound such a weapon could inflict.

4. The verb *slá* — "to strike (a blow)", is also used of scything hay, and here there is a pun on the two senses. This remark and Mar's reply may, as Hermann Pálsson has suggested (*Maal og Minne* 1979) be base on an incident in Snorri's *Saga of Olaf Tryggvason*, ch. 108 (see *Heimskringla* I, ed. Bjarni Aðalbjarnarson, *Íslenzk fornrit* XXVI, Reykjavík 1941, pp. 362–3).

But when Helga, Glum's sister, heard the news she went to Thvera and asked how her son had behaved. Glum said: "There was nobody braver."

Then she said: "I'd like to see his body, if there's nothing else for it." That was granted her, and she had him lifted up into a cart and carefully treated, and when she came home she bathed his wound and bandaged it afterwards, and his consciousness returned, so that he was able to speak to people.

The law when equal numbers of men fell on both sides was that they should be said to cancel out, even if there was thought to be some difference in importance between them, but that a side which had suffered heavier casualties should choose the man whose case was to be prosecuted. But if something happened later in the case which made it seem that it would have been better to have chosen differently, the choice should not then be altered. So when Thorarin heard that Thorvald Chatterbox was still alive, he chose to prosecute for the killing of his brother Thorvald Hook. But a little later he heard that that had been assigned to Gudbrand, and then he would rather have chosen someone else, but now had to continue with the choice that had already been made. He and Einar Eyjolfsson now met, and Thorarin recalled the agreement they had made between them.

Einar replied: "My attitude is the same as before, when Bard was killed." Now Einar took charge of the case to conduct it at the Assembly in the summer, and prosecuted Glum.[5] Thorarin lay wounded all summer and so did Thorvald Chatterbox, but both recovered.

Glum had a large force at the Assembly, as had both sides. An attempt at a settlement was now made by distinguished relatives of both sides, and

---

5. This could mean merely that Einar is leading the Espihol side (in at least two cases — against Steinolf for seduction and against Gudbrand for the slaying of Thorvald Hook, though Glum is not personally the defendant in either). Alternatively, it may be a prosecution of Glum himself for having started the battle by hurling his spear at Arngrim.

the resulting agreement was that the killing of Steinolf should be paid for by cancelling the outlawry of Vigfus Glumsson. But Gudbrand was convicted of the killing of Thorvald, and Glum arranged for him to go abroad. They went home with things like that, and Thorvard and Thorarin were displeased, and Thorarin thought he'd got no satisfaction for the killing of his brother Thorvald. Now Glum enjoyed a high reputation. During the following winter a verse began to circulate which Glum had just composed:

7. The goddess asks of my actions,
   The girl, the wine keep's keeper,
   But it's not in the mouths of men,
   Such murmurs of murder are over.
   For me, who enlivened the raven,
   My linen-lass, that lies finished,
   (And as they now lie counted, the count of them lies.)[6]

CHAPTER 24

ONE DAY WHEN people were at the bath at Hrafnagil Thorvard arrived there. He was a very entertaining man and took pleasure in a great many things. He said: "What's become of the people who used to be able to amuse us with new stories?"

---

6. Prose sense: "The woman asks about my deeds; murder is not in men's speech — those things were long ago. Woman, the matter is fully settled for the warrior..." The last two lines are lost and the original ending must have been equivocal. I have therefore added one ambiguous line for continuity of sense, without trying to make the stanza look complete.

Concealing a killing was discreditable, and such verses as this may satisfy the legalistic need to "justify" oneself by announcing the crime (though not legally) and at the same time they allow the poet to outwit his enemies. There may also be an element of "showing off" to any third party clever enough to understand the verse, and perhaps also some bravado in taking the risk of being found out. For another example, see *Gísla saga* ch. 18.

They said: "All the pleasure and fun is where you are."

He said: "Nothing gives me greater pleasure nowadays than reciting Glum's verses. But I'm puzzled about what he thinks has been counted short in one verse where he says he's been credited with too few killings. What are we to think about how that could be? And is it more likely that Gudbrand might have killed Thorvald, or that Glum did?"

That line of argument seemed convincing to a lot of people. Now he went to see Thorarin and said:

"I've been thinking a bit, and it seems to me that the truth hasn't come out about the killing of Thorvald Hook, because it can be seen in Glum's poetry that he thinks he's been counted a bit short on killings."

Thorarin said: "I can hardly take up the case a second time, even supposing this were true. It will have to stay quiet now."

"That's not a good idea, though it might have been allowed to lapse if the matter hadn't been dug up again. But now I'll make sure people know about it, and you'll get so much disgrace as a result that no one will ever have had more."

Thorarin said: "It seems to me that the case will be hard to pursue at the General Assembly because of the strength of Glum's relatives."

Thorvard said: "I can suggest a plan to get round that. Summon him to the assembly at Hegranes[1]. You've got strong support from your relatives there, and it'll be difficult for him to defend the case."

Thorarin replied: "That's the plan we'll adopt." With that they parted.

Now the spring weather was bad and everything became hard to get. In the spring Thorarin prepared a case against Glum at the Assembly at Hegranes, because all the chiefs whose duty it was to hold the local Assembly there were bound by kinship with Thorarin; but it was almost impossible to come over the moors on horseback because of the snow.

---

1. It would have been illegal to summon Glum to the spring local Assembly at Hegranes in Skagafjord when all parties in the dispute came from Eyjafjord, but the Quarter Assembly for the Northern Quarter may be meant — see Introduction p. 19.

Glum resorted to putting a[2] large cargo vessel in the charge of his brother Thorstein, who was to make his way westwards and come to the Assembly with armour and supplies. But when they got opposite Ulfsdal they wrecked the ship and everything was lost there — men, goods and all. Glum went to the Assembly with 120 men and didn't manage to camp any nearer than the outer margins of the court area[3]. Einar Eyjolfsson had arrived there with the Espihol men.

Word was sent to Glum that he should come and produce a legal defence for himself. So Glum went, but no more room was allowed than one man might walk through; forces were drawn up on both sides and Glum was told to run the gauntlet between them if he wanted to get to the court. But that seemed inadvisable to him, and he said to his men: "Now it's easy to see that they think they have us in the hollow of their hand, and perhaps they're right. But I don't want you to turn back all the same; I'll go first, and then two abreast behind me, and four abreast behind them, and we'll run forward with our spears in front of us, and the wedge will go in if it's driven hard." They did so, and in a single rush ran into the circle of the court, and it was late into the evening before they were driven away, so large and dense was the crowd there. At last the court was convened a second time; but when they began to sum up the case, Glum went to the Assembly slope and named his witnesses that the sun had then touched the horizon of the Assembly field. Then he used the legal veto to prevent anyone from judging cases, and at that every case that was then in progress had to lapse.

---

2. *einn* ("one", "a"), not legible with the naked eye in M., can be deciphered under ultra-violet light.

3. *fjörbaugsgarðr* — the word usually refers to the sentence passed on a lesser outlaw, but seems originally to have been used of the three places where such a man was protected, then of the distance (bowshot range) within which he was "safe", then, perhaps as here, simply as a measure of distance. But it could here be a specific outer area in which lesser outlaws and others who could not enter the Assembly because of the sanctity of the place were allowed to conduct their business.

117

People rode away, and the Espihol men were very annoyed about it. Thorarin said Glum had behaved disgracefully to them.

Einar replied: "It doesn't seem so dreadful to me as to you, because the case can be taken up again from the point at which it lapsed."

Then the Espihol men rode to the General Assembly with Einar and many friends of theirs who had promised them support against Glum. Glum's relatives helped him to get his legal rights in the case, and it was settled on the advice of wise men, if Glum would take an oath about the case to swear that he didn't kill Thorvald Hook. And as a lot of people mediated, they agreed that Glum should take an oath that he hadn't killed Thorvald Hook, and it was specified precisely that the oath should be taken five weeks before the beginning of winter[4]. And now the case was pursued so strongly that they were going to go through with the prosecution unless he would take the oath at three temples in Eyjafjord, and he would be liable to the legal penalty for failing to take an oath if it wasn't forthcoming. There was a lot of talk about this case, about what Glum's oaths would be like or how they would be delivered.

CHAPTER 25

About Glum's Oaths

NOW PEOPLE RODE home from the Assembly and Glum stayed at home throughout the summer, and all was quiet in the district. The local meeting came round, and people rode to the meeting; but Glum stayed away from it, so that nothing was heard of him. Mar stayed at home on the farm, but five weeks before the beginning of winter he sent out

---

4. The first day of winter, by the modern calendar, would be the Saturday between October 21st and 27th, and by the Julian calendar in use in medieval Europe between October 10th and 17th. The oath was therefore to be taken between 16th and 22nd September by modern reckoning, and eleven days earlier by the medieval calendar.

invitations, as a wedding had been arranged there, and no fewer than 120 people came to the feast. Everyone thought this invitation strange, because those for whom it was held were of little importance. That evening people there saw men riding in twos and threes out of all the valleys in Eyjafjord, and gathering together into an army, which came down into the neighbourhood, and Glum and Asgrim and Gizur had arrived with 360 men, and they came to Thvera for the night and stayed for the feast.

Next morning Glum sent word to Thorarin and told him to come to Djupadal not later than mid-morning[1] to hear the oaths. Thorarin reacted quickly and got hold of 120 men. But when they came to the temple, six men went into it — Gizur and Asgrim with Glum and Einar and Hlenni the Old with Thorarin. The man who was to take a temple oath used to take in his hand a silver ring reddened in the blood of a sacrificed ox, and weighing not less than 3 ounces.[2] Then Glum spoke these words, that "I name Asgrim as witness and secondly Gizur as witness that I take a temple oath on the ring and I deny to the god, that I was not there and did not strike there and did not redden point or edge where Thorvald Hook met

---

1. "Mid morning" was about 6 a.m. At the main farm in Djupadal (now called Storidalur), some ruins in the meadow are believed locally to be those of the temple, but this tradition is at best dubious.

2. The Old English Chronicle supplies contemporary evidence of oaths sworn "on the holy ring" by the viking leaders in England in 876 (see *The Parker Chronicle 832–900*, ed. A.H. Smith, London 1935, p. 30; *The Anglo-Saxon Chronicle* trans. G.N. Garmonsway, London (Everyman) 1953, p. 74). The ring is supposed to have lain on each temple altar and to have been worn by the priest when consecrating Assemblies, but sources differ as to its minimum weight — *Landnámabók* says two ounces, while *Eyrbyggja saga* ch. 4 says two or twenty ounces (in various MSS) and *Kjalnesinga saga* ch. 2 simply calls it a large ring. But Olaf Olsen has argued powerfully that all of these are related, learned Christian guesses (*Hørg, Hov og Kirke* pp. 35–49, English summary pp. 227–8). Some stipulations about the weight of the ring and its reddening with the blood of a sacrificed animal may be historical, but its association with heathen temples is unlikely.

his death. Let those who are wise men standing by look to the oath."[3] Thorarin and his friends weren't prepared to find fault, but they said they hadn't heard that form of words used before. In the same way the oaths were taken at Gnupafell and also at Thvera. Gizur and Asgrim stayed at Thvera for some days, and at parting Glum gave Gizur the black cloak and Asgrim the gold-inlaid spear, and they parted friends.

During the winter Thorvard and Thorarin met, and Thorvard asked: "Did Glum take the oath alright?"

Thorarin replied: "We didn't find anything wrong with it."

Thorvard said: "It's remarkable that clever men can be so easily fooled. I've known people announcing killings to be their own work, but I've never known or heard of anyone taking an oath that he'd killed somebody, as Glum has done — and what more could he have said than to affirm that he struck there and was present there and reddened point and edge where Thorvald Hook fell at Hrisateig? — even if he didn't put it in the most usual words — and that disgrace to you will be remembered ever afterwards."

Thorarin replied: "I didn't take it like that, and besides, I'm tired of having to deal with Glum."

Thorvard said: "If you decide you're getting tired of it because of ill health, then let Einar take up the case again. He is clever and of noble family, and many people will support him. Gudmund doesn't sit idle where his brother is concerned, and getting himself into possession of Thvera is the thing Einar wants most."

After that Thorarin and Einar met and co-ordinated their plans, and Thorarin said: "If you take charge of the case many people will help you. What's more, I'll arrange for you to buy the land at no higher price than

---

3. Glum's oath depends on the preposition *at* having the same form as a poetic negative suffix, so that *ek vark at þar* — "I was at that place" and *ek varkat þar* "I was not there" sound identical. Glum's opponents expect a denial, so they do not notice the obvious prosaic sense.

Glum paid Thorkel the Tall for it."

Einar replied: "Glum has now given away the things his grandfather Vigfus gave him, the cloak and spear which he told him to keep if he wanted to hold onto his position, saying it would decline after he let them go. Now I'll take up the case and follow it through."

CHAPTER 26
More about the case

N̲OW EINAR ONCE more prepared the case for the killing with a view to prosecution at the General Assembly, and both sides gathered in great numbers. But before Glum rode away from home he dreamed that large numbers of people had come to Thvera to meet Frey, and that he saw a large crowd on the gravel banks beside the river, while Frey sat on a throne. He dreamed that he asked who had come there. They replied: "These are your bygone kinsmen, and now we're asking Frey that you may not be driven off the land at Thvera, but it's no use, for Frey answers shortly and angrily and remembers now Thorkel the Tall's gift of an ox." He woke up — and Glum said his feelings for Frey were the worse ever afterwards.

People rode to the Assembly, and the outcome of the case was that Glum admitted the killing, and his friends and relatives exerted their influence so that there might be a settlement rather than that outlawry or exile should result. And they were reconciled at the Assembly by Glum giving half the land at Thvera to Ketill, the son of Thorvald Hook, in compensation for his father, and selling half for what it was worth; but he was to stay there throughout that winter and then was to be banished from the area and not allowed to live any nearer to it than Hörgardal. After that they went away from the Assembly. Later Einar bought the land as he had been promised.

In the spring Einar's men arrived there to work the land, and Einar said that they must tell him every word Glum said. One day Glum got into conversation with them and said:

"It's easy to see that Einar has got himself some good labourers, and the work on the land is well done. Now it's very important that great and small matters should alike be attended to. You ought to put up a beam to hang washing on, here beside the river where it's convenient for the women to do the heavy washing — for the wells by the farmhouse are bad." Now they came home and Einar asked what conversation they had had with Glum. They said how attentive he was to everything that ought to be done. He said:

"Did you think he really wanted to get things ready nicely for me?" They replied: "That's how it seems to us."[1]

Einar said: "It doesn't look that way to me. I think he would have strung you up on that beam, and was intending to raise up a monument to insult me.[2] But now you're not to go again."

Einar moved house there in the spring, but Glum stayed there until the last day for moving on. When they were ready to leave, Glum sat down in the high seat and made no move to depart, even though he was shouted for. He had the hall hung with tapestries and refused to part with the land like a mere peasant. Hallbera the daughter of Thorodd Hjalmsson[3] was

---

1. Glum and Einar address the servants with the plural pronoun forms þér, yðr (used to three people or more), but the servants refer to themselves with the dual okkr — "the two of us". Confusion between dual and plural only became common during the 16th century — we should perhaps emend okkr to the plural oss, and assume at least three servants. Further see Helgi Guðmundsson — *The Pronominal Dual in Icelandic*, Reykjavik 1972 (University of Iceland Publications in Linguistics No. 2), especially pp. 21, 29, 64, 125–6.
2. *reisa níð* — to put up a "pole of insult", cf. *Egils saga* ch. 57, where a magic curse is being made; elsewhere the magic element is often forgotten, but the insult remains (see *Gísla saga* ch. 2, *Reykdæla saga* ch. 25, and Folke Ström,"*Níð, ergi* and Old Norse moral attitudes" (Dorothea Coke Memorial lecture, 1973, London 1974). Glum may have intended to curse Einar's possession of the land and ensure that he be driven from it by magic.

the mother of Gudmund and Einar. She then lived at Hanakamb. She came to Thvera and greeted Glum and said:

"I wish you good luck Glum, sitting there, but you can't stay here any longer. Now I've marked out the lands of Thvera with fire,[4] and I turn you out now, both you and yours, for the land is dedicated to my son Einar." Then Glum rose up and told her to go on nattering, despicable woman. But nonetheless, Glum then rode away, and happening to look over his shoulder to the farm, recited a verse:

8. I cleared my way like the earls —
    — word spread of that, men heard
    Of my storm-shaken trees of Odin,
    Heard of my swordsmen's branches stirred by my hand.
    But now I've slain, you warrior
    Who send men to Odin's reception
    And with the steel wand beckon —
    To its bounds I've dashed the broad land out of my hand.[5]

---

3. In *Landnámabók* and *Njáls saga* ch. 113, Hjálmr ("helmet") is the nickname of Hallbera's father rather than the name of her grandfather; the scribe of M. appears to have miscopied *Hjálms* as *Hjálms s.* — "H's s(on)".

4. Carrying fire round one's boundaries or shooting a fiery arrow over them (cf. *Eyrbyggja saga* ch. 4 and *Landnámabók*) probably had religious as well as legal significance, and may have been believed to bring the local spirits under one's control — cf. J. de Vries, *Altgermanische Religionsgeschichte*, 2 vols. Berlin 1956–7, I pp. 295–6.

5. Prose sense: "I cleared my way with my warriors like the earls in ancient times — my fame spread. Now at last by killing I have thrown away the broad land with its borders, warrior."

The first half of this verse is quoted by Snorri Sturluson in *Skáldskaparmál* ch. 47 — see Introduction pp. 11, 24. For a detailed investigation of this stanza, with the suggestion that it is influenced by the Eddic poem *Rigsþula* and may have been part of a brief prose-and-verse sequence which preceded the saga as we now have it and was its major source, see Ursula Dronke, "*Sem jarlar forðum*. The influence of *Rigsþula* on two saga-episodes", *Speculum Norroenum* (see ch. 3 note 1 above), pp. 56–72, especially pp. 57–64. Her hypothesis is quite possible, but hard to test.

Glum farmed at Mödruvellir in Hörgardal along with Thorgrim Blizzard, but put up with that no more than one year. Then he lived for two years in Myrkardal. Then a landslide crashed down near the farmhouse there, so that it swept away part of the buildings. Then Glum recited a verse:

9. ... No further joy
    Will the generous necklace giver have
    Since it came on us, wide ranging
    Woe and loss from one blow.
    When for forty years we'd been happy,
    You feeder of blood's seagulls
    Mar with your spear, now it's less,
    Splintered is my domain, after forty winters.[6]

Then Glum bought land at Thverbrekka in Öxnadal and stayed there for the rest of his life, and lived to become old and blind.

---

6. Prose sense: "(I), the generous patron, will not enjoy happiness again — a great calamity has come home to us from one blow, when we had sat happily for forty years, warrior; now my domain is smaller."

One or two syllables are missing at the beginning; the best addition is *mála* — "of the times" ("I shall not enjoy again the happiness of the times... when... we'd sat at home ..."), but even this is only a guess, and I have not tried to fill the gap.

Fleinmarar – (1.5) "of the spear's sea" (ie. blood). M. has *fleymarar*, which does not make sense in context.

The "warrior" kenning in the second half of this verse, literally "he who feeds the seagull of blood (lit. "the spear's sea")," may contain a pun between *mar* — "seagull", and the name of Glum's son Mar, to whom the verse might have been addressed.

setr (1.8) — "domain" — M. has *sex* — "six"; apparently due to the following *tigu* (going with *fjóra* in 1.5 to make "forty") — *sextigu* would mean "sixty". The scribe was trying to make sense of the verse without understanding its construction.

CHAPTER 27

About Narfi from Hrisey

THERE WAS A man called Narfi who lived on the island of Hrisey. He had been married to Ulfeid, the daughter of Ingjald, son of Helgi the Lean. Their sons were Eyjolf, Klæng, Thorbrand and Thorvald. They were all very able men and relatives of Glum. Klæng and Eyjolf went on living on Hrisey after their father. There was a man living at Hagi called Thorvald and nicknamed the Manly, and he was married to a daughter of Thord Hrafnsson of Stokkahladir who was called Helga.[1]

One spring Thorvald came from Hagi to Hrisey in a cargo vessel, intending to go fishing, and when Klæng heard about that he joined him in the expedition. But when they got out of the fjord they found a recently dead whale, fastened ropes to it and towed it in along the fjord in the course of the day. Klæng wanted to take it to Hrisey, because that was a shorter distance than to Hagi, but Thorvald wanted to take it to Hagi and said that was just as legal. Klæng said it was against the law to move it anywhere except to the nearest land belonging to one of those involved.[2] Thorvald said that he was justified and declared that Glum's kinsmen needn't encroach on his rights — "and whatever the law says, the stronger side are going to have their way this time." Thorvald had

---

1. The relationship between this paragraph and the differing but related material in *Landnámabók* is extremely complicated — cf. Turville-Petre ed., Introduction pp. xxxviii–xlii, and *Íslenzk fornrit* IX, pp. XXVII–XXXV.
2. Flotsam whales were valuable, and there are several cases in the sagas of disputes over them, eg. *Fóstbræðra saga* ch. 7. Klæng quotes the law accurately — see *Grágás* II, p. 131.

more men on that occasion and they took the drifting whale from Klæng by force, although both of them were landowners. Klæng went home and was very annoyed about it; Thorvald and his party laughed at Klæng and his men and reckoned that they wouldn't dare do anything about it.

One morning Klæng got up early and went with three other men in to Hagi — he got there early, when people were still asleep. Then Klæng said:

"Now we must work out a plan. There are some cattle here beside the farmyard, and we'll drive them up onto the building[3] Thorvald's sleeping in and in that way entice him out."

They did so, and Thorvald woke up and dashed out. Klæng rushed at him and gave him a fatal wound, and then quickly went away, not daring to announce the killing there because there were a lot of people about; so he went home out to the island and announced the killing there. Now it fell to Thorarin and Thord to prosecute. They said it had been murder. And when this case came before the Assembly, Glum stayed at home, but during the Assembly he went out to Fljot and into Svarfadardal and asked for support at the court of confiscation, but gave instructions that this intention be kept secret. Klaufi of Bard said:

"We'll certainly give Glum support" — he was married to Halldora, daughter of Arnor Red Cheek — and many others promised Glum their support. Now Glum went home.

The case went ahead at the Assembly, and afterwards they set off for the court of confiscation with four ships and thirty men on each, and

---

3. The traditional Icelandic house had low side walls and a pitched roof covered with turf, on which livestock could jump up and graze, but which their weight could hardly fail to damage — hence Thorvald's haste to remove them. This method of construction continued until quite recently in Iceland, and some examples of it can still be seen (see eg. *Grettis saga*, trans. Denton Fox and Hermann Pálsson, fig. 10).

4. As there are four ships and only three names, M. may have omitted a name here, most likely either Gudmund the Powerful or Hlenni the Old.

Einar, Thorarin and Thord were in command of the ships.[4] They came out to the island at dawn and saw smoke over the buildings, and Einar asked whether it seemed to them, as it did to him, that the smoke was not completely blue. They agreed. Einar said:

"It seems to me from the smoke as if it must be very crowded in the buildings, and the steam must be rising off men. But we'll make an experiment to see if that's the case, and row ostentatiously away from the island, and then we'll find out whether it is crowded." And so they did. But when the men on the island saw that, they rushed out to the ships and set off after them. And Glum had come there with 240 men, and they chased them all the way in to Oddaeyrr, and the court of confiscation was not held, and the men of Eyjafjord were disgraced by the incident.

Glum stayed on his farm throughout the summer. It was also his responsibility to consecrate the autumn Assembly, but the Assembly place is on the east side of the fjord, not far from Kaupang, and the Eyjafjord people collected a very large number of men, while Glum had only thirty. Many people tried to persuade Glum not to go with so few men. He replied:

"The best part of my life must be over now, but I'm glad to say that they haven't so completely routed me that I can't behave properly." Glum went by ship in along the fjord and came ashore to the booths.[5] There are steep gravel banks and loose stones there between the fjord and the booths. And when Glum came opposite the booth that belonged to Einar, men came running out of the booths and rushed at them with shields and shoved them off the gravel banks, and Glum fell and rolled with his shield down to the level shingle at the bottom, and wasn't wounded at all, but three spears had stuck fast in his shield. Thorvald

---

5. The booths (as at the General Assembly) were small, permanent but roofless structures of turf and stone, uninhabited except during Assemblies, when they were covered over with sheets of canvas. They were also erected at trading centres, see. ch. 11 note 1.

Chatterbox had then just reached the shore, saw that things were going badly for Glum, and leapt ashore taking an oar in his hand. He ran up onto the gravel bank and lashed out at Gudmund the Powerful with the oar; it hit his shield, smashing it in half. Part of the oar[6] hit him on the chest, and he fell unconscious and was carried to his booth on a stretcher by four men. Then each side dared the other to attack, and they hurled missiles at each other and fought with stones, and there was a hard fight and many were wounded; and everyone agreed that a small number couldn't have defended themselves more stoutly than Glum and his men. Einar and his forces attacked fiercely. Then people went between them, and it finished with two of Glum's men dead — Klæng Narfason and Grim Bankleg, the brother of Halldora, Glum's wife. Then Brusi Hallason recited this verse:

> 10. Honours are even in slaying
> I hear, with the ship-borne steersmen,
> Like trees on their wood-planked steeds,
> — You warlike girl in your headdress — it's equal shares.
> Yet I think that forest of swordsmen
> Whose flame cleaves the ship-rail shield,
> Compared with what I'd expected
> You linen-decked putter of questions, were cast down much faster.[7]

Einar recited a verse:

> 11. The forcer was forced at Assembly

---

6. M. *árar-hlutrinn* — "part of the oar"; some paper MSS and early editors emend to *árar-hlumrinn* — "the handle of the oar", but this seems unnecessary.

7. Prose sense: "We have an equal share in battles with the sailors, woman — that's what I hear word of. But I think the warriors went much harder down the bank than I had expected, woman."

With his thin edged snake of steel, to flee
Down through the storming seamen
Down the steep slope — he could not be easily stopped —
— To the stones that edge the ships' highway,
The strand where sea steeds land,
Nor could the spear-stinging warrior
Stand sure with his stallion-hoof on the shingly shore.[8]

Then Glum recited a verse against this one:

12. They halted, the army with helmets,
    Hats of hanged Odin, from battle;
    It did not seem pleasant, that plunge,
    The possible rush down the slope, the risk of loss.
    While we stood out on the gravel,
    The eager blood-icicle's keepers,
    And the raven gorged his meal
    Of gore, where shielded we stood on the shore.[9]

The case was settled by the killings of Klæng and Thorvald of Hagi being set against each other. The killing of Grim Bankleg was also equated with the injury to Gudmund, and Glum was ill-pleased by the outcome of the case, as he said in a verse which he composed afterwards:

---

8. Prose sense: "The warrior had to flee at the Assembly; he was not easily stopped by the steep gravel bank in battle, when he, the warrior, could not fasten his hoof on the shingle by the sea's edge."

9. Prose sense: "The army with helmets was reluctant to go over the bank; it did not seem pleasant to them to risk it, when we stood with our shields on the sand bank, eager for battle. The raven received a meal of blood."

The two halves of this verse are preserved separately (the first half twice) in Snorri's *Skáldskaparmál*, chs. 2, 46, 57, and in *Þórðarbók*, a late version of *Landnámabók*; this is fortunate, for M.'s text is very corrupt and largely meaningless. I follow Snorri's text except in 1.6, where M. is clearer and more evocative.

13. Evil is all on earth,
    Age curses, the poet rages.
    Long past and lost, for the most part
    My life, in blind blizzards of endless striving,
    While far from eddying bloodshed
    Brave Bankleg lies unthanked —
    No goddess, to make Grim glad,
    Grimly can gather my vengeance for him.[10]

One summer,[11] when the brothers Gudmund and Einar were riding home from the Assembly, Glum invited people to his house and sent men up to Öxnadal Heath to invite the brothers. And he said that he now wanted to be completely reconciled with them, "because I'm not able to achieve anything now because of old age, and I won't invite them only for a meal." Glum was now blind. He had a watch kept on their progress. Gudmund wanted to accept the invitation, but Einar didn't, and they rode along on opposite sides of the river. Glum was told that one of the two parties was coming. "Then Einar can't be willing to accept the invitation — he's so suspicious that he trust nobody." It's said that Einar shouted across to Gudmund and said: "If you go tonight, I'll be there tomorrow." And Gudmund thought over what he had said:

"Then your meaning must be that you would have to prosecute the case after my death."[12] Now he turned to follow Einar. Glum was told

---

10. Prose sense: "It has turned out badly on earth, old age harms the poet much; most of my life has passed in the turmoil of battle, now that I cannot avenge the brave Grim Bankleg in battle because of men."

11. The editors and several late paper MSS begin a new chapter here, although there is no indication of this in either M. or the longer version of the saga. I prefer to follow the authoritative MSS. in taking the whole of Glum's career after his fall as a single chapter.

12. Gudmund interprets Einar's remark, correctly, as an unspoken pun; if his brother "came" the morning after himself he would "speak after" him; the phrasal verb *mæla eptir* means both "to speak after someone" and "to prosecute the case for someone's killing".

that neither group was coming. "That's bad," said Glum, "because I'd expected that if I went to meet them I shouldn't miss them both." He had a drawn dagger under his cloak. And that was the end of the encounters between Glum and the people of Eyjafjord.

But when Christianity came to Iceland Glum received baptism and lived for three years after that, and was confirmed during his final illness by Bishop Kol and died in the white robes of a convert.[13] Mar Glumsson was then living at Fornhagi, where he had had a church built,[14] and Glum was buried there, and also Mar when he died, and many other people, because for a long time there was no church in Hörgardal except that one. It's said that for twenty years Glum had been the greatest chief in Eyjafjord, and for another twenty years nobody was more than equal with him. People say also that Glum was the hardiest of all fighting men in this country.

And here ends the story of Glum.

---

13. These were worn for a week after the ceremony (more usually after baptism) — cf. the *Tale of Thorvald Chatterbox* and *Laxdæla saga* ch. 40.

14. There are remains of what appear to be a church and churchyard wall in the home meadow at Fornhagi, and local tradition may be correct in supposing this to be Mar's church, but no thorough excavation has yet been done.

THE TALE OF ÖGMUND BASH

At that time there were many well-born people in Iceland who were related to King Olaf Tryggvason.[1] One of them was Viga-Glum, the son of Eyjolf the Lump and of Astrid, the daughter of the nobleman Vigfus, as has been said already. The sister of Viga-Glum was called Helga — she was married to Steingrim of Sigluvik. Their son was called Thorvald, nicknamed Chatterbox.

There was a man called Ögmund who had grown up with Viga-Glum; he was the son of Hrafn, who was at that time a rich man and lived up north[2] in Skagafjord. He had been a slave of Glum and his mother Astrid, and Glum had given him his freedom, so that Hrafn was his freedman. Ögmund's mother's family came from Guddal and her name is not known, but she was related to Viga-Glum. Ögmund was a fine man to look at, big and able, and was treated with great favour by his kinsman Glum. Glum had by now declined into old age and lived at Thverbrekka in Öxnadal by the time his kinsman Ögmund had grown up; but Glum's son Vigfus was at that time with Earl Hakon[3] in Norway.

---

1. On Olaf Tryggvason, see *Viga-Glums saga* ch. 5 note 1; this version of the story is taken from the "great" saga about him, where it is ch. 174.
2. So most MSS, because Skagafjord is in the northern quarter, but *Flateyjarbók* (F) says "west", taking the viewpoint of Glum's household in Eyjafjord. The fragment interpolated into the longer version of *Viga-Glums saga* adds that Hrafn had been foreman of the slandered slaves in *Viga-Glums saga* ch. 7.
3. Earl Hakon Sigurdarson of Hladir, effective ruler of Norway from about 975–95, the predecessor of Olaf Tryggvason and a steadfast heathen. It is essential to this story that it begins at the end of Hakon's reign, and thus correct that Glum should now be living at

One spring Ögmund told Glum that he was eager to go abroad. "I'd like," he said, "to buy myself a ship at Gasar. I'll use my father's money, which will be enough, but I'd like practical help and a word of support from you."

Glum replied: "Lots of people go abroad who are no more promising than you. Now it seems important to me that you should get honour and reputation from the journey rather than a lot of money, if you can't get both." Glum bought a ship for him from some Norwegians, and Ögmund made ready for his journey with a lot of goods which his father gave him. Ögmund was to be captain of this ship and its crew, who were mostly Icelanders going abroad for the first time. They put to sea rather late in the summer and the breeze was good to them — they got a strong following wind. But when the ocean had been crossed, they sighted land late in the day, and the breeze was blowing towards the land. Then the Norwegians who were navigating said that it would be more prudent to strike sail, let the ship drift overnight, and then sail to land in daylight.

Ögmund replied: "We mustn't waste such a fair wind — it's not certain that it will be the same in the morning, and there's plenty of moonlight tonight." They did as he ordered and sailed on. But when they were a short way from land, there lay in front of them a large number of longships fastened together at their moorings in a channel between two islands, and they didn't see the ships before they ran one down, and thus sailed on into harbour on the mainland. Then some of the men who were aboard the merchant ship said that they had sailed carelessly, but Ögmund replied that it was up to every man to mind his own business. But the command of those longships was held under Earl Hakon, while the ship they had sunk belonged to a man called Hallvard, a powerful man and the

---

Thverbrekka; but the version in *Viga-Glums saga* inserts it into the middle of Glum's career, and thus makes Ögmund return to Thvera after his first expedition (ie. before about 986). This leaves the interpolator with a chronological problem, and how he solved it we do not know, since the fragment breaks off before that point.

Earl's greatest friend. All the goods that had been on the ship were lost, but the crew were saved. The Earl was told first thing in the morning what disgrace and injury had been done to them. He became very angry at this piece of news and spoke in these terms:

"These men must be idiots who've never been to a foreign country before. Now I give you leave, Hallvard, to punish them and take revenge for your grievances, because they can only be the sort of men that it won't be beyond you to deal with. You're not without either the courage or the strength to do them as much damage or more, whoever they are."

Then Vigfus Viga-Glumsson replied: "You must surely, my lord, be prepared to accept reparation from these men and let them stay alive, if they are willing to submit to whatever damages you award. Now I'll go and find out who they are and try to arrange a settlement if that is possible."

The Earl replied: "You may do that, but I think they'll find that I'll come down pretty heavily on them in assessing damages for such a serious offence."

Vigfus went to the merchant ship and recognised his relative Ögmund there, greeted him warmly and asked for news from Iceland about his father. Ögmund gave him the information he had asked for. Then Vigfus said:

"You're going to get into serious trouble because of this accident." Then Vigfus told him what had happened, and also that Earl Hakon had been reluctant to allow mediation with them. "Now it's my business with you here, kinsman, to ask you to submit to the Earl's judgement. I'll put forward[4] your side of the case as well as I can, and then it may pass off well, at least to some extent."

Ögmund replied: "From all I've heard about this Earl, I ought not to

---

4. The longer version of *Viga-Glums saga* and most MSS of *Ólafs saga* have *flytja* — "put forward", "present", which seems more sensible than *byrja* — "begin", "open", preferred in *Íslenzk fornrit* IX.

place my whole future in his power, least of all if he makes threats, because he'll certainly carry them out. But I won't refuse if he speaks moderately about it."

Vigfus replied: "You might consider what it would be sensible for you to do, because you're dealing with someone whose anger you can't resist if you refuse to accept his decision."

Vigfus went out to the Earl's ship and told him that these men were his foster brothers and some of them his relatives — "and they're willing to put their case in your hands."

Then one of the Earl's men retorted: "You're telling your lord a lie, Vigfus — they're making no sensible offer for themselves."

Hallvard answered: "The truth of the matter is that I ought to take my revenge myself and not have to involve other people in it."

The Earl told him to do that.

Vigfus said: "If I can manage it I'll be the death of anyone who kills my kinsman Ögmund."

Hallvard answered: "You Icelanders may be enormously brave, but it can still be expected in this country that people who have any self respect won't put up with being insulted without compensation, whether by you relatives of Viga-Glum or by anyone else."

Then Hallvard rowed towards the merchant ship, while the Earl ordered a close watch to be kept on Vigfus. Hallvard came to the merchant ship and asked who was captain there. Ögmund gave his name. Then Hallvard said:

"My friends and I have a serious grievance against you, and we've come here now to find out if you'll offer any reasonable damages."

Ögmund answered: "You won't be refused damages if your demands aren't excessive."

Hallvard said: "The men involved in this are not going to accept anything small in settlement of such a major injury."

Ögmund said: "We'll refuse to compensate at all if there's arrogant behaviour on the other side."

"I've no intention," said Hallvard, "of pleading for what you ought to offer." Then he leapt up onto the merchant ship and struck Ögmund a hefty blow with the back of his axe, so that he fell senseless at once. With that, Hallvard went to see the Earl and told him about it, but the Earl said he'd done much less about it than would have been proper.

Hallvard answered: "Their leader was the main villain of the piece, and I didn't feel like doing any more this time than knocking him silly. It was fitting that disgrace should be the payment for disgraceful behaviour, and the revenge can always be added to later if it seems necessary." But as soon as Vigfus heard about that he got very worked up and wanted to fight Hallvard or to kill him if he could get the chance; but the Earl gave orders that he be watched, so that he got no opportunity.

Ögmund came round, although he had been seriously injured and lay ill far into the winter; but he recovered eventually and was much mocked because of this incident, so that wherever he went he was nicknamed Ögmund Bash — but he behaved as if he knew nothing about what was being said. Vigfus often visited him and urged him to take vengeance. "I'll give you my support," he said, "in putting a stop to your disgrace."

Ögmund replied: "There's no reason to take the matter as far as that, kinsman — it seems to me that I've suffered no more disgrace in this business than Hallvard, and less could hardly be expected, considering how obstinately we conducted our side of things at first. It would be unwise to take vengeance for this, seeing Hallvard is a great friend of Earl Hakon and you're here under his rule. I ought to repay your father Glum better than by putting you in such danger that certain maiming or death could be expected for you as a result of my interference."

Vigfus replied: "I give you no thanks, and my father won't either, for claiming to be looking after my interests when I don't want to myself. I suspect it's cowardice more than prudence that brings you to this, and it's bad to give backing to a man who's got the heart of a hare in his chest. It seems too that you take after your long line of slave ancestors more than the Thvera men."

They parted, with Vigfus in a great rage. The winter and the spring passed away. Then Ögmund made ready his ship and went out to Iceland in the summer, and he had acquired a lot of wealth on this trip. He sailed his ship into Eyjafjord. Glum soon heard about the ship's arrival; he was also told at once the disgrace Ögmund had suffered. But when Ögmund had made arrangements for his ship and property he went to Thverbrekka and stayed with Glum for a while. Glum had little to say to him, and it could be seen that he was not grateful for his visit. Ögmund was in the best of spirits and strutted about a great deal. He went to all the social gatherings and was rather inclined to meddle in people's affairs, and if any quarrels arose nobody was quicker with great solutions than Ögmund. He was also given to involving himself in everything Glum needed in management of the farm or supplies, and held the most splendid opinion of himself, but for a long time Glum wouldn't speak to him.

And one day Glum said to him: "You must know, Ögmund, that I give you no thanks for your labour, and I'm amazed that you're so self-assertive and meddlesome in other people's business, seeing there's no courage in you. And that first trip of yours was a disgrace, so that I would rather not see you again when you're willing to accept shame for yourself and reproach for all your relations, and to be called a coward ever afterwards because you daren't take your revenge."

Ögmund replied: "You ought to consider, kinsman, what influenced me when the chance of vengeance was passed over; I thought too much was at risk, in the safety of your son Vigfus."

"You shouldn't have considered that," said Glum, "when he didn't want to himself. It would have seemed worth it to me to have you both dead, provided you'd shown your courage by taking vengeance. Now either you're more patient and long-suffering than most other people, but you'll show your manhood, albeit rather belatedly, by being less pusillanimous in your behaviour another time; or else you're completely useless, the worse influences in you will get the upper hand, and it'll turn out as it often does, that a man sprung from slaves proves incapable of noble behaviour. But anyway, I won't have you with me any longer."

Then Ögmund went to his father's.

But when he had been two years in Iceland, he made ready his ship and took on men for it and sailed to Norway, making landfall in the north, in the Trondheim district, and continuing in along the fjord.[5] He moored his ship late in the day off Nidarholm. After that Ögmund said: "Lower a boat now. I'll row up into the river and get news of the country."

Ögmund put on a parti-coloured cloak with hand-worked gold embroidery at the seams — it was an object of great value. He got into a boat with two other men — it was early in the morning — and they rowed in to the quay. There was a man walking down to the river from the town, wearing a hooded mantle made of scarlet and embroidered all over. The hooded man walked down to the quayside and asked who was in charge of the boat. Ögmund gave his name. The townsman said: "Are you Ögmund Bash?"

"Some people call me that," he said, "and what's your name?"

He replied: "I'm called Gunnar Half and Half — and that's my nickname because I like wearing parti-coloured clothes."

Ögmund said: "What news is there in this country?"

Gunnar answered: "The main news at the moment is that Earl Hakon is dead, and an excellent king, Olaf Tryggvason, has come to power."

Ögmund said: "What do you know about a man called Hallvard, a man of great family and wealth from Trondheim province?"

Gunnar replied: "It's not strange that you should ask about him. He's now known as Hallvard Neck, because he was in the battle against the

---

5. The Trondheim fjord, leading in to the town of Nidaros (modern Trondheim) at the mouth of the river Nid. The medieval port was bounded by the fjord to the north and by the curving river to the east and south, and had its quays along the lower part of the river. The island of Nidarholm lies out in the fjord north of the town; Ögmund anchors between it and the town in the evening and takes his dinghy up into the river next morning to get to the quay.

Jomsvikings with Earl Hakon last year,[6] and there he got a large wound on the neck, behind the ear, and he's carried his head on one side ever since. He's here in the town with King Olaf now, and has been enjoying good favour from him. But you've got a good cloak, Ögmund, and in fine colours, seeing it's parti-coloured — will you sell it to me?"

Ögmund replied: "I won't sell you the cloak, but if you like it I'll give it to you."

"Give it to me then and good luck to you for it," said Gunnar, "and I'd like to be able to repay you for this gift, but you must first accept this hooded mantle. Perhaps it may be of use to you."

Then Gunnar went a bit further up into the town wearing the cloak, but Ögmund put on the mantle. He said to his men: "Now you must tie the boat loosely to the bank by the sternpost, so that it doesn't drift while I go ashore; but you must sit in your places and keep the oars ready to start rowing." Then Ögmund went up through the town walls and saw little sign of anyone. He saw open doors in an inn, and inside some men standing by some wash basins; one was particularly big and handsome, and carried his head on one side, and Ögmund realised from Gunnar's description that it must be Hallvard. Ögmund went to the doors, and all those inside thought they recognised him as Gunnar Half and Half. Speaking in rather a low voice, he asked Hallvard to come out to him for a moment — "because I have a confidential and urgent message for you," he said. Then he turned away from the doorway on the other side and drew the sword he was carrying. Everyone there was acquainted with Gunnar Half and Half, and Hallvard went out by himself; but Ögmund

---

6. For this famous battle, in which Vigfus Glumsson is said to have taken part, see *Ólafs saga Tryggvasonar* (in Snorri's *Heimskringla*) chs. 35–42 and *Jómsvíkinga saga*. Icelandic tradition consistently, as here, dates the battle to 994, a year or less before Olaf Tryggvason came to power, but the Danish historian Saxo Grammaticus places it in the reign of King Harald Bluetooth of Denmark (died 986), and this is more probably correct (see *Íslenzk fornrit* XXVI, Inngangur p. CXII).

struck him a fatal blow as soon as he came up to him. Then he rushed down to the boat, threw off the mantle, put a stone in the hood and flung it out into the river, where it sank to the bottom. Ögmund got into the boat and told them to row out of the river. When they got to the merchant ship he said to his men: "There's great disorder in this country, and now the wind is blowing out along the fjord — we'll hoist sail and sail back to Iceland." They said he was rather timorous,[7] when he didn't dare land just because the local inhabitants were quarrelling among themselves. But they did as he ordered, came back to Iceland and reached Eyjafjord. Ögmund went to see Viga-Glum, told him about his trip and said that the revenge had been taken, even if the delay had been long. Then Glum was pleased and said he had always felt that Ögmund would turn out to be a worthwhile man in the end. Then Ögmund stayed over the winter with Glum and was in good favour with him.

Meanwhile, when it seemed to Hallvard's men that he was a long time coming back, they went out and found him lying dead in a pool of his own blood. Then this piece of news was told to King Olaf, and with it, as people thought was the case, that Gunnar Half and Half had killed him.

The King replied: "I wouldn't have thought it at all likely from him, but nonetheless he must be searched for in the town at once and hanged if he is responsible for this."

Gunnar Half and Half had a brother called Sigurd; he was rich and one of King Olaf's bodyguard, and very dear to him. Sigurd was there in the town. But when he found out that his brother had been condemned to death, he went to look for him and found him. Sigurd asked him if he really was guilty of this deed of which he was accused. Gunnar said far from it.

Sigurd said: "People think it's true all the same, so tell me, what do you know about this event?"

---

7. So *Íslenzk fornrit*. IX; some MSS. add, rather pointedly, "as before", and this could be original.

Gunnar replied: "I'm not telling that at the moment either to you or to anyone else."

Sigurd said: "Get yourself out of here then."

Gunnar did so, reached the forest and couldn't be found. Afterwards he went eastwards over the mountains through Oppland, hiding all the way; he didn't break his journey until he got all the way east into Sweden.

Great heathen sacrifices were held there at that time, and for a long while Frey had been the god who was worshipped most there[8] — and so much power had been gained by Frey's statue that the devil used to speak to people out of the mouth of the idol, and a young and beautiful woman had been obtained to serve Frey. It was the faith of the local people that Frey was alive, as seemed to some extent to be the case, and they thought he would need to have a sexual relationship with his wife; along with Frey she was to have complete control over the temple settlement and all that belonged to it. Gunnar Half and Half finally got as far as there and asked Frey's wife to help him, suggesting that she might let him stay there. She looked him over and asked who he was. He said he was a travelling man of low degree and from a foreign land. She said: "You can't be an altogether fortunate man, for Frey does not look with a friendly eye on

---

8. Adam of Bremen (writing ca. 1075) describes the great temple (still heathen in his time) at Uppsala, the Swedish capital, saying that Thor was the most important cult there, but that Wotan (Odin) and Frikko (Frey) were also worshipped (*Gesta Hammaburgensis ecclesiae pontificum* IV, 26–7, ed. B. Schmeidler, Hanover and Leipzig 1917, pp. 257–60; trans. F.J. Tschan, New York 1959, pp. 207–8). But the worship of Frey was particularly associated with Sweden, and Adam may be wrong about the primacy of Thor (Turville-Petre, *Myth and Religion of the North*, p. 169). The fertility deity with a consort of the opposite sex whose idol is taken on an annual progress is also found in the goddess Nerthus (cf. Frey's father Njörd) in Tacitus's *Germania* ch. 40 (ed. J.G.C. Anderson, Oxford 1938, and see his pp. 187–9; trans. H. Mattingly in *Tacitus on Britain and Germany*, London 1948, pp. 133–4); a similar divine progress probably took place from Uppsala (Jan de Vries, *Altgermanische Religionsgeschichte* I, p. 473). Adam of Bremen was known to some learned Icelanders by ca. 1200, but he does not include the annual progress of the god, and some more direct contact with the Swedish traditions is likely here.

you. Now rest here for three nights at first, and then we'll see how Frey takes to you."

Gunnar replied: "I'd much rather accept your help and protection than Frey's." Gunnar was entertaining and a great storyteller. But when three nights had passed, Gunnar asked Frey's wife what was to happen then about his staying there.

"I don't know for certain," she said. "You're destitute, yet it may be that you're of good family all the same, and for that reason I would like to give you some help; but Frey has little use for you, and I fear he would be angry. Now stay here a fortnight, and then we'll see what happens."

Gunnar said: "So far it's turning out just as I would have chosen, that Frey hates me but you are helping me, because I think he's a real devil and a half."

Gunnar got on with people better the longer he stayed there, because of his entertaining conversation and other excellent qualities. Once more he came to speak with Frey's wife and asked about his position. She answered: "People have taken a liking to you, and I think it would be a good idea for you to stay here over the winter and go to the feasts with Frey and me when he goes to ensure good crops for the people — yet he dislikes you."

Gunnar thanked her cordially.

Now it came to the time that they set out from home, and Frey and his wife were to sit in a cart while their retainers walked in front. They had far to go over some mountain tracks. Then a great blizzard of snow came upon them; the journey became difficult, but Gunnar was ordered to go with the cart and lead the carthorse. But at last it came to the point that the whole force drifted away from them, so that only Gunnar was left, with Frey and his wife in the cart. Then Gunnar began to get very tired as he was leading the carthorse; and when that had gone on for a while, he gave up leading and sat down in the cart, allowing the beast to choose its own way. A little later she said to Gunnar: "Make another effort and lead the horse, or else Frey will attack you." He did so for a bit, but when he became very tired once again, he said: "Now I'll risk having to stand up to Frey if he comes at me." Then Frey got out of the cart and they began to wrestle, and Gunnar was much too weak. He saw that this would never do. Then he thought to himself that if he could manage to overcome this demon and it was granted to him to get back to Norway, then he would turn back to the true faith and be reconciled with King Olaf if he was willing to accept him. And immediately after this thought Frey began to reel before him, and next he fell. Then the devil which had been hidden in the idol went rushing out of it, and only a hollow log of wood was left — and he broke that to pieces. Afterwards he gave the woman two choices — either he would abandon her and look out for himself, or else she was to say when they came to settled country that he was Frey. She said she would much rather say that. Then he put on the clothes of the idol, and the weather began to clear.

At last they came to the feast which had been prepared for them; many of the men who ought to have come with them were present. Now it seemed to the people an omen of great importance that Frey had shown his power by bringing himself into settled lands with his wife in such weather that everyone had fled from them, and what was more, that he could now walk with other men, and ate and drank like other people. They went round to feasts throughout the winter. Frey was always very silent with other people. But it did happen that he wouldn't allow living beasts to be slaughtered before him as before, and would accept no sacrifice and no oblations or offerings except gold and silver, good clothing or other precious things. But when some time had passed, it became clear that Frey's wife was pregnant. That was taken to be excellent, and the Swedes were now delighted with this god of theirs; the weather too was mild and all the crops so promising that nobody could remember the like. This news of how powerful the heathen god of the Swedes was spread far and wide through the world. It also reached King Olaf Tryggvason, and he had his suspicions about what it meant. And one day in the spring King Olaf summoned Sigurd, brother of Gunnar Half and Half, to talk with him. The King asked if he had heard any news of his brother Gunnar. Sigurd said he had heard nothing of him. The King said: "It's my belief that this heathen god of the Swedes about whom so many stories are going round and whom they call Frey must in fact be your brother Gunnar, because the strongest heathen cults are when living men are worshipped. Now I want to send you east to fetch him, for it's a shameful thing to know of a Christian man's soul going so sorely astray. I will give up my anger against him if he is prepared to come into my presence of his own free will, because I know now that it was Ögmund Bash who killed Hallvard, and not Gunnar." Sigurd took prompt action and went to find this Frey, and recognised in him his brother Gunnar. He conveyed King Olaf's message to him and told him what he had said.

Gunnar replied: "I would be glad to go and make my peace with King Olaf, but if the Swedes realise what's going on they'll want to put me to death."

Sigurd said: "We'll steal away from here secretly and have faith that the luck and goodwill of King Olaf will with God's mercy be able to do more than the malice and pursuit of the Swedes, as it surely will." Gunnar made ready himself and his wife, and they took with them such moveable property as they could travel with, and after that set out secretly by night. When the Swedes found out about this they were able to see all that must have happened, and they immediately sent men after them. But when they had travelled a short distance the Swedes lost their way and so did not find them; with that they went back. Sigurd and the other two did not break their journey before they came to King Olaf. He took Gunnar back into friendship with him and had his wife baptised, and after that they kept to the true faith.

THE TALE OF THORVALD CHATTERBOX

In this same summer which has just been described[1]
Thorvald Chatterbox, the nephew of Viga-Glum, came to Norway
from out in Iceland. He was a handsome man, tall and strong and
generous with money. Thorvald made landfall in Trondheim province
and put in to Nidaros. King Olaf was present in the town, having just
arrived from the south of the country; and when the King heard that some
heathen merchants had arrived from Iceland he invited Thorvald to meet
him and asked him to allow himself to be baptised. Thorvald agreed, in
order to gain the King's friendship, to be baptised and accept Christianity.
The King said that he should win his friendship all the more completely
for having so readily agreed to his request. Thorvald and his shipmates
were then baptised, and he stayed with the King in a honoured position
throughout the winter.

There was a retainer of the King called Sigurd and another called
Helgi; both were worthy men in themselves and dear to the King, yet
they were very different in character. Sigurd was popular with everyone,
but Helgi was unjust and secretive. It was arranged for Thorvald
Chatterbox to sit between them in the hall throughout the winter. Helgi
envied Thorvald and tried to discredit him at every opportunity, but
Sigurd was kind to him — and Helgi abandoned the bench and wouldn't
sit beside Thorvald and Sigurd. Then he began to slander Thorvald to the

---

1. ie. in the "Great" saga of Olaf Tryggvason, the summer of the year 998. This tale is
ch. 201 of that saga.

King as much as he could, to the point where the King told him to stop. "There's no need for you," said the King, "to slander Thorvald either to me or to other people who are with me, because I would rather make my own judgements about my men." Then Helgi tried to see if Sigurd could be estranged from Thorvald, and slandered him to him. Sigurd replied: "I shan't fall out with Thorvald as a result of your words, because I've found him to be a good fellow, but you're malicious."

Now because Helgi still didn't stop but rather was intent on persisting with the slander, it came about at last that the King became distant towards Thorvald. One day Helgi said to Thorvald: "Ask the King why he is so silent."

Thorvald replied: "I'm not going to do it just because of your word or urging, and I don't expect the King believes your slander, even if something is making him displeased with me."

Helgi said: "So the bumpkin's still full of his own importance."

Some time later Thorvald said one day, when he came before the King: "My Lord, I must make so bold as to ask about your unhappiness. If it's caused by illness then the remedy is hard to see; if some other anxiety or some event due to human behaviour is the cause, then perhaps it may be put right with the help of your good luck and personal spirit."[2]

The King replied: "I'm not sick."

Thorvald said: "Then we're further on at once, since the worst is ruled out. Has anyone offended you?"

The King said that was it — "and it can be avenged, but you have an obligation to solve this difficulty, since you asked about it first."

Thorvald said: "All your men are bound to do whatever you

---

2. *gipt* — "good luck", appears to be the same as *gæfa* — see *Viga-Glums saga* ch. 4 note 4. For *hamingja* — "personal spirit", see ch. 9 note 1. Belief in such spirits seems not to have disappeared with the coming of Christianity, and they sometimes became fused with a rather ill-understood version of the Christian concept of the soul — see Turville-Petre, *Myth and Religion of the North* pp. 229–30.

command, but I ought to know what is involved in this, even though I may be ill-equipped to put it right."

The King said: "There's a man called Bard the Stout, whose family comes from Oppland and who has plenty of money. He has an only child, a daughter called Thora. Bard has become rather old — he lives in Oppland at a place called Ulfarsdalir and has a large and splendid farm. His daughter Thora is with him, but people don't know of any large numbers of people there. Now I'm not best pleased that Bard will neither accept the faith nor come to see me. Twice I have sent parties of twelve men to him, and none of them have come back."

Thorvald said: "Is this Bard a great one for heathen sacrifices?"

The King replied: "Not as far as is known, because there's no temple on his farm, but he is regarded as very strange, and his customs and behaviour are unknown."

Thorvald said: "I'd be glad to bring you happiness, my Lord. Now I'll go to visit Bard if you wish, whatever else comes of it."

The King said that was what he wanted. Helgi was pleased at that, because he expected that Thorvald wouldn't come back, any more than the others who had gone on this journey.

After that Thorvald got ready, and the King told him to take as many men as he wanted. Thorvald answered: "I've found by experience that Sigurd, my companion at table, is a reliable and good man; I'd like him to go with me, but no one else, because your good luck and personal spirit, my Lord, can do more for us than any number of men."

The King replied: "Certainly I shall send my good will with you. But I want to send you to a farmer called Björn who lives not far from Bard — he seems to me the likeliest man to be able to tell you something of Bard's habits and to show you the way to him."

Then they set off and came to Björn, and he received them well as soon as he knew that they were the King's messengers. They asked him about Bard's household and customs. Björn said his affairs were managed in a remarkable way — "There's no sign of any men when one gets there, but all the jobs are done properly and well."

During the night, when they had gone to sleep, Thorvald dreamed that King Olaf appeared to him and said: "You'll find a napkin by your head when you wake up, and wrapped up in it is a letter in which are written the names of God.[3] In the morning you must place that letter on your chest and wind the napkin over it and round your body as far as it will stretch. Then you'll be able to go boldly to meet Bard."

Thorvald woke, found the napkin and arranged it as he had been instructed. In the morning Björn the farmer accompanied them away from the steading and showed them the way to Bard's farm. There were some woods to go through, but when they came out of the woods they saw a large farm with a high wattle fence around it; they went to the farm. The five-barred gate in the fence was open, as were the doors to the buildings. They saw nobody outside. They went into the porch and looked round. There were spacious rooms and newly-planed planking for the internal partitions. On one side was a hall, all hung with tapestries and well furnished. Bard sat on the high seat — he was bald, dressed in scarlet clothes and holding deerskin gloves, and a tall handsome woman sat sewing at the table; they saw nobody else. Bard said: "What's come into the porch?"

They gave their names and said they were the King's men. Bard said:

---

3. Interest in the names of God stretches back at least as far as St. Jerome (ca. 340–420), who wrote a commentary on ten names taken from the Old Testament (*De Deo et Nominibus Ejus*, ed. J.P. Migne in *Patrologia Latina*, vol. 23, Paris 1865, cols. 1365–8). Fifty-six names of God appear in a Latin hymn from ca. 900 attributed to Notker Balbulus beginning *Alma chorus Domini*, and King Sverrir of Norway is said to have sung a version of this during a battle in 1181 (*Sverris saga* ch. 50, *Flateyjarbók* text only — see *Flateyjarbók*, ed. S. Nordal and others, Akranes 1944–5, vol. III, pp. 198–9). But the commonest prayer in the later middle ages appears to have been one containing seventy-two names of God, and a late 16th-century Icelandic example of this survives, on a leaf of parchment intended to be wrapped round oneself as a charm against boils. Further, see Peter Foote, *Nafn guðs hit hæsta* (article in English in *Speculum Norroenum* — see ch. 3 note 1 above — pp. 139–54).

"What errand have you here, just the two of you together?"

Thorvald answered: "Our force outside the door is quite big enough to bring you to see the King by force if you won't go of your own free will."

Bard then twisted the gloves between his hands and recited this:

1. Now I thought that I'd fought
    Enough to have taught
    That alone I can master
    This runt of a boaster.

Thorvald said: "Let's try now and see, then, and set to." Then Thorvald set upon Bard and they wrestled fiercely; much of the day had then passed. They struggled for a time, and Thorvald became very exhausted. Then he silently prayed to God to give him some strength against him, but Bard went on attacking as hard as ever; yet when their chests came together it was as if someone had gone up to Bard and snatched his feet from under him, so that he fell over the threshold. He and Thorvald were then both so weary that they couldn't go on. Then Bard said: "Now you show your worth, Thora."

She answered: "I can't help you father, because Sigurd and I have been wrestling, and it's been a very good contest, with the two of us equally strong."

Bard said: "Then it's necessary now to resort to something I haven't needed to do before, to ask for help against a single individual — let those who live in the undercroft now come forth and help me." At that forty men leapt out; Thorvald and Sigurd were seized. Bard said: "Those who live under the hall have helped me well, Thora, and so they will again if I need anything — so it seems sensible to me that Sigurd and his friend should not be bound; but all the same I don't want you rushing at me again, you troll, even if you do call yourself Thorvald, because you're not lacking in courage and skill. Yet perhaps you may be called a man, in which case you must be rather skilled in witchcraft, for I had no lack of strength against you earlier. But I think you must have called up such mighty spirits against me that I fell before them, for it has never happened before that I've been thrown by a single man. But you'll have to stay here tonight, even though you may be afraid about what's going to be done with you."

Then a well-laid table was set before them — neither food nor good drink was lacking there. But when they had eaten their fill, Bard said: "I don't begrudge you the food, but I would have thought the two of you had fed pretty splendidly even if you had been men with nothing to fear whatever and were among friends." Then they were escorted to bed, and they slept well that night.

In the morning, when they were ready to leave, Bard told his men to escort them away from the farmstead. But when they had come away, Thorvald looked round and saw nobody beside them. Then he said: "Bard, now, would like us to go away and have nothing more to do with him, but that's not to be; we'll go back to see him, just as before."

Then they went in. Bard said: "You're pretty odd characters, walking out but not going away. Why are you incapable of being afraid like other people — are you absolutely determined to die?"

Thorvald answered: "We have returned again because I wasn't willing to put an end to my own good name or your advancement. We're certainly not so frightened as not to dare carry out the King's mission to its conclusion. Now I want to ask you to go voluntarily with me to meet the King."

Bard said: "Why don't you ask first what faith I hold ?"

"Because I'm not curious about it," said Thorvald.

Bard said: "I'll make it known to you all the same, that I don't trust in any idol or devil. I've gone from one country to another and met both giants and black men, and they none of them got the better of me; so I have long trusted in my own strength and ability. But now I have been deceived in that belief for the first time, and I can see that you wouldn't have overcome me if you had been using nothing but your own powers; so what was on your chest when our breast-bones met? I have a suspicion that the being who caused that result must be able to do much."

Thorvald answered: "You're right to consider Him powerful, because it was the names of the God we Christians believe in."

Bard said: "I can't but imagine that he must be able to do anything if he sets about it in person, when the thing that completely overcame me was only his names; and I'll go with you to meet the King for this reason, that I can see that it must be a good thing to trust in such a powerful god if one must trust in any at all. But the reason why I had the undercroft built and put my men in it was because I intended, if a body of men was sent against me, to make use of them and take advantage of my superior numbers. But if only two or three came to me, I wasn't worried, because I thought I wouldn't find myself at their mercy. And here are King Olaf's twenty-four men that he sent to me; they've all been well looked after here, and not killed as the King must have thought."

After that Bard got ready and went with Thorvald and all his men to see the King. But when they got near the town of Nidaros, Bard said: "You go to the King now, Thorvald, and tell him we want to be baptised here where we've got to now, because I don't want the mob to laugh when I'm undressed at such a great age." Thorvald went to the King and told him all about his journey and what the outcome had been. King Olaf was pleased at that and went at once with his clerics to meet Bard. Bard greeted the King warmly and said: "You control a mighty god, my Lord King, and because I've proved the truth of that I'm now willing to trust in him and let myself be baptised."

The King replied: "You speak well Bard, according to your understanding, but the true way of putting it is that He is a mighty God who rules me and all things, visible and invisible, and calls to Him, albeit in various ways, all those who are worthy of His service."

Then Bard and all his men were baptised. Bard said: "Tell me, King, whether I'm saved now."

The King said he was.

Bard said: "I've thought myself very self-sufficient up to now and served neither Kings nor other noblemen, but now I want to become your supporter, King, and follow you as long as I live. That seems to me the best hope of not losing the salvation I've now got. But I want you to take charge of my daughter Thora and all her property and marry her to Thorvald the Icelander, because we have much to repay him for."

Thorvald replied: "That can't happen, because I'm already married in Iceland."[4]

The King said: "Then you must give this woman to your friend Sigurd; they'll make a good match, being equally strong."

Thorvald replied: "I'll gladly do that. But I'd like to be assured by you, my Lord, that you'll turn Helgi out of your service — and even at that the difference shown between him and Sigurd will be too little. But for your sake I won't do anything else against Helgi if you grant me this."

The King said that so it should be.

Afterwards Sigurd married Thora and settled on the farm in Oppland that Bard the Stout had had. Bard took ill shortly after he was baptised and died in the white robes of a convert. But Thorvald went to Iceland covered with honour by King Olaf and was considered a fine man and very brave.

---

4. No wife is known for Thorvald — this detail may be intended simply to contribute to the comic tone of the end of the tale.

Translations of Icelandic Texts Mentioned in the Notes

(Chapter numbers in the notes are those of the standard Icelandic language editions — for sagas of Icelanders, *Heimskringla* and *Landnámabók*, the series *Íslenzk fornrit* (Reykjavík 1933–); for most legendary sagas, *Fornaldarsögur Norðurlanda*, ed. Guðni Jónsson and Bjarni Vilhjálmsson, 3 vols., Reykjavík 1943–4. For other editions see notes. Chapter divisions in the translations are not always exactly the same. Asterisked translations have appeared in paperback editions).

1. *Áns saga bogsveigis*
No published translation; a typescript translation is included in S.F.D. Hughes, "*Áns rímur bogsveigis*: Two Nineteenth Century Icelandic Metrical Romances" (University of Washington dissertation 1972).

2. *Atlamál* (in the *Poetic Edda*)
ed. and trans. Ursula Dronke, in *The Poetic Edda* vol. I, Oxford 1969.
trans. L.M. Hollander, Austin 1928.
selections trans. P.B. Taylor and W.H. Auden, London 1969.*

3. *Bjarnar saga Hitdœlakappa*
No English translation; in German in F. Niedner, *Vier Skaldengeschichten* (*Thule* IX, Jena 1914, new ed. 1922).

4. *Egils saga*
trans. Gwyn Jones, Syracuse University Press for the American-Scandinavian Foundation, 1960.
trans. Christine Fell with poems trans. by John Lucas, London and Toronto 1975. *
trans. Hermann Pálsson and Paul Edwards, London 1976.*

5. *Eyrbyggja saga*
trans. Hermann Pálsson and Paul Edwards, Edinburgh 1973.*

6. *Fóstbræðra saga*
trans. L.M. Hollander in *The Sagas of Kormak and the Sworn Brothers*, Princeton University Press for the American-Scandinavian Foundation, 1949.

7. *Gísla saga*
trans. George Johnston with a tailpiece essay by Peter Foote, London 1963.*

8. *The "Great" saga of Olaf Tryggvason*
trans. J. Sephton, London 1895.

9. *Grettis saga*
trans. Denton Fox and Hermann Pálsson, University of Toronto 1974.*

10. *Hávamál* ("The Words of the High One," in the *Poetic Edda*) ed. and trans. D.E. Martin Clarke, Cambridge 1923.
trans. Hollander, Austin 1928.

11. *Heiðarvíga saga*
trans. William Morris and Eiríkur Magnússon in *The Story of the Ere-Dwellers*, London 1892.

12. *Heimskringla*, by Snorri Sturluson (including, among others, *Ynglinga saga*, *The saga of Olaf Tryggvason*, *The saga of St. Olaf*) trans. S. Laing, originally London 1844; reprinted as *Heimskringla: The Olaf Sagas*, 2 vols. (Everyman) London 1915, and *Heimskringla: Sagas of the Norse Kings* (Everyman) London 1930.
trans. L.M. Hollander, Austin 1964.

13. *Hrafnkels saga*
trans. Gwyn Jones in *Eirik the Red and other Icelandic Sagas*, London 1961.
trans. Hermann Pálsson in *Hrafnkel's saga and other stories*, London 1971.*

14. *Hrólfs saga Gautrekssonar*
trans. Hermann Pálsson and Paul Edwards, Edinburgh 1972.*

15. *Hungrvaka*
ed. and trans. Gudbrandur Vigfússon and F. York Powell in *Origines Islandicae*, 2 vols., Oxford 1905.

16. *Íslendingabók* by Ari Thorgilsson
ed. and trans. Halldór Hermannsson (*Islandica* XX), New York 1930.

17. *Jómsvíkinga saga*
ed. and trans. N.F. Blake, London 1962.

18. *Kjalnesinga saga*
trans. Gwyn Jones as *The Saga of the men of Keelness*, in *Four Icelandic Sagas*, Princeton University Press for the American-Scandinavian Foundation, 1935.

19. *Kormáks saga*
see no. 6 above.

20. *Landnámabók*
trans. Hermann Pálsson and Paul Edwards as *The Book of Settlements*, University of Manitoba Icelandic Studies No. 1, Winnipeg 1972.

21. *Laxdæla saga*
trans. Margaret Arent, New York 1964.
trans. Magnús Magnússon and Hermann Pálsson, London 1969.*

22. *Ljósvetninga saga*
partial English trans. in *Origines Islandicae* (see No. 15 above); in German by W. Ranisch and W.H. Vogt, in *Fünf Geschichten aus dem östlichen Nordland* (*Thule* XI), Jena 1921, 2nd ed. 1964.

23. *Njáls saga*
trans. Magnús Magnússon and Hermann Pálsson, London 1960.*

24. *Reykdæla saga*
No English trans.; in German in *Fünf Geschichten*, see No. 22 above.

25. *Snorra Edda* (The Prose Edda), by Snorri Sturluson (consisting of *Prologue, Gylfaginning, Skáldskaparmál, Háttatal*)
Prologue and Gylfaginning ed. A. Faulkes, Oxford 1982.
No complete translation; abridged trans. by J.I. Young, London 1954.

26. *Sturlunga saga*, chiefly by Sturla Thordarson
trans. Julia H. McGrew and R. George Thomas, 2 vols., American-Scandinavian foundation, New York 1970–4.

27. *Sverris saga*, chiefly by Abbot Karl Jónsson
trans. J. Sephton, London 1895.

28. *þiðreks saga* (The story of Dietrich von Bern)
No English trans.; in German by W. Baetke (*Die Geschichte Thidreks von Bern*) (*Thule* XXII), Jena 1924.

29. *Vatnsdæla saga*
trans. Gwyn Jones, Princeton University Press for the American-Scandinavian Foundation, 1944.

30. *Völsunga saga*
ed. and trans. R.G. Finch, London 1965.
trans. William Morris and Eiríkur Magnússon, London 1870; reprinted by the Kelmscott Press 1901.

Further, see Donald Fry, *Norse Sagas Translated into English, A Bibliography*, New York 1980.

Genealogies

The Thvera Family

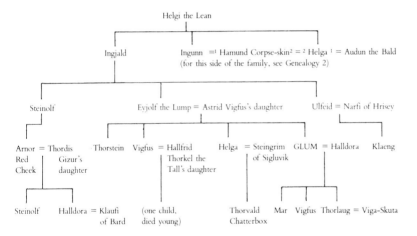

The Espihol Family

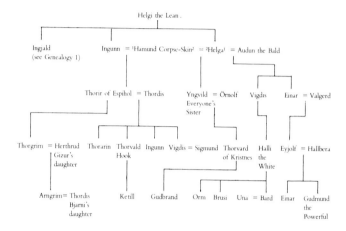

Glum's Maternal Relatives

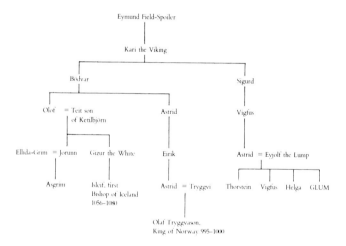

158

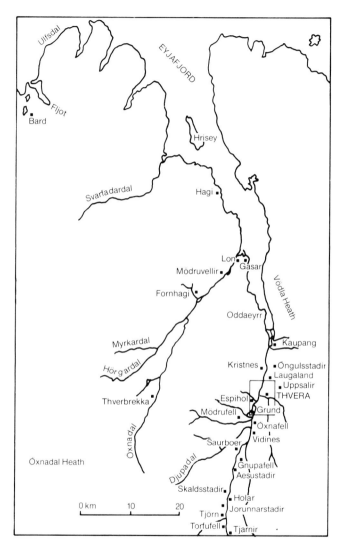

Map 2:EYJAFJORD
   (for area inside small square, see Map 3)

159

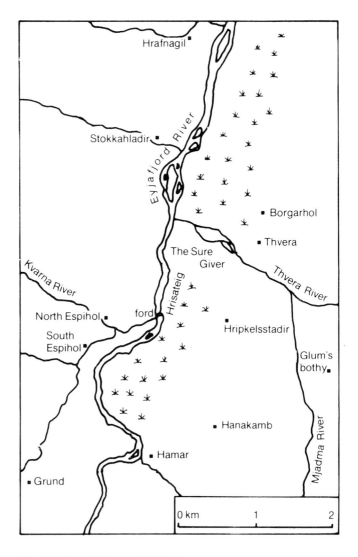

Map 3: THE THVERA DISTRICT